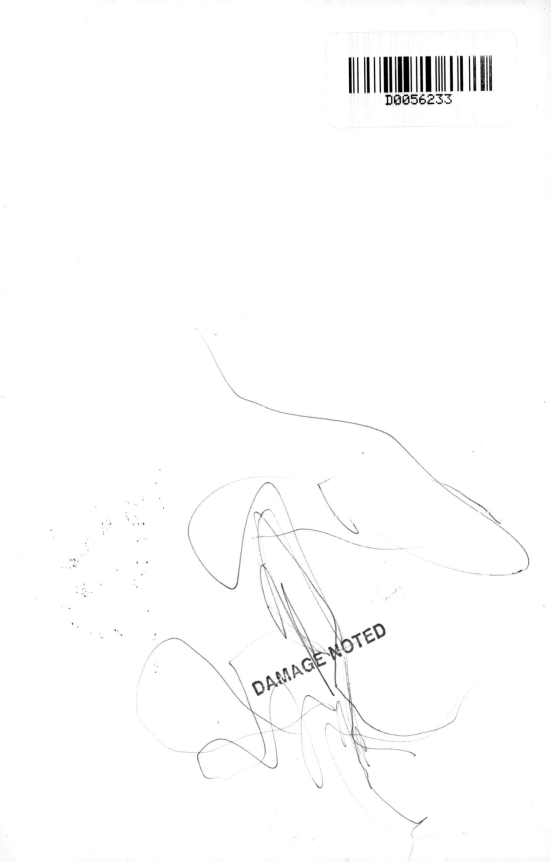

◂ SOUL OF THE WORLD ▸

CHRISTOPHER DEWDNEY

▴

SOUL
OF THE
WORLD

▴

UNLOCKING THE
SECRETS OF TIME

HarperCollins*Publishers*Ltd

Soul of the World
© 2008 by Christopher Dewdney. All rights reserved.

Published by HarperCollins Publishers Ltd.

First edition

Excerpts from earlier versions of this book were published in
The Walrus (April 2006) and the *Toronto Star* (July 16, 2006).

HarperCollins books may be purchased for educational, business,
or sales promotional use through our Special Markets Department.

HarperCollins Publishers Ltd
2 Bloor Street East, 20th Floor
Toronto, Ontario, Canada
M4W 1A8

www.harpercollins.ca

Library and Archives Canada Cataloguing in Publication

Dewdney, Christopher, 1951–
Soul of the world : unlocking the secrets of time /
Christopher Dewdney.

ISBN 978-1-55468-002-3

1. Time. 2. Time—Folklore. 3. Time—Social aspects.
4. Time in literature. 5. Time perception. I. Title.

QB209.D48 2008   304.2′37   C2007-906581-3

HC 9 8 7 6 5 4 3 2 1

Printed and bound in the United States

Text design by Sharon Kish

Pythagoras, when he was asked what time was,
answered that it was the soul of this world.
—*Plutarch*, Platonic Questions

Contents

THE PRESENT

THE PAST

THE FUTURE

◀ THE PRESENT ▶

Chapter One

THE ANGEL OF NOW: TIME'S NATURE

You mean *now?*
—*Yogi Berra, after being asked what time it was*

The night was cool—too cool to stay outside for very long—yet a slight mildness in the air pledged warmer evenings to come. In the twilight I could make out the long rectangle of my lawn and a dark strip of earth where winter flowerbeds ran along the east fence towards the silhouette of the garage with its peaked roof. Two stubborn patches of snow glowed whitely at its foot. Then something stirred, breathlessly close. Something gathered and clotted in the darkness near the top of the fence. It fluttered with an inky, soft movement made eerily precise by its silence.

A bird had alighted. I couldn't see it at first. I searched along the top rail and there it was—I met the full intensity of its eyes before I could name it—an owl, a small one, perched on the top of a fence post less than twelve feet from where I stood. We stared at each other, both motionless, me in spellbound astonishment and the owl broadcasting its hooded, imperious and unblinking gaze. I wanted to get closer. I think I even had the naive idea that the owl might hop onto my arm if I offered it. But after I had taken a few cautious steps it rose up as soundlessly as it had arrived, floating up into the stars above a neighbour's house and disappearing into the night. How marvellous! This mysterious bird had blessed my yard.

That night, for one moment in time, the owl and I were aware of each other—we met in an enchanted encounter that ended too quickly for me. Something ancient bonded us. Blood and miracle and twilight had combined in a single charged alchemy, and I had, briefly, been in the presence of magnificence, of night's own beak and talons. Out of darkness, out of the endlessly random permutations of time and place, a wonder had occurred. Time had stood still. The owl, with its moondial face, had brushed its wing over the flow of time. For those few seconds I had been completely in the moment—oblivious of future and past, my senses alive to the night, the owl, the beating of my own heart.

The next day I got out my old set of vinyl transfer letters and stuck the word "owl" in one-inch-tall letters at the top of the fence post. I wanted to fix the place where the owl had landed, and I wanted to memorialize this special moment in time. I had experienced a present so spellbinding it was if an invisible door had opened onto eternity.

◂ ◂ ◂

Time gives and time takes away. That evening has been carried off by time, along with all the other events of that day and that week. The dust-speckled snow that lingered for few more days in the shadow of the garage, like the terminal moraine of a diminutive glacier, has disappeared, and the green tongues of crocuses have begun to poke through the surface of my garden. A new season has started. This year on March 20 at 7:34 a.m. Eastern Standard Time, spring officially began. Our timekeepers, trained over the millennia to capture the exact instant of equinoxes and solstices, announced the subtle moment of transition—the beginning of a new season and a signpost along earth's 584-million-mile journey around the sun. Yet the cycles of the seasons themselves roll through the calendar like cogs caught in time's great wheel.

In my yard the incremental passage from winter to spring seems gradual, but I'm already behind the seasonal schedule. My lawn needs raking and the bricks that line the flowerbeds have buckled in the frost and need resetting. I tell myself that I can do these chores next week, though the rising greenery in my garden has an urgent timetable that will eventually force me to act. I hear spring ticking like a clock. Is time against me or is it on my side? What does it have in mind for me?

◂ ◂ ◂

Time is more than "just one damn thing after another," as an anonymous wit once quipped. It is more than a sequence of events. Without time there is nothing. Time is both the dance floor and the music. Everything that moves and everything that seems unmoved is choreographed by time. It is everywhere. The world we live in and the universe that surrounds it could not exist without the architecture of time. Only time, with its one-way flow, allows us to accomplish anything. Even thought depends on time—if time stopped, we would become nothing more than frozen, unconscious statues. Perhaps that is why the Greeks thought that their god of time, Cronos, presided over thought itself. Time is like an animating breath. Time, with its promise of a continual future, is also the wellspring of hope, for only within time can our imaginings be realized.

Often it feels as though time gushes, that it pushes me up and I hover like a ball floating on top of a fountain or a geyser. I can feel the tremendous energy of it, and of life also. The past few afternoons have been bright and warm beneath a hazy blue sky. Yesterday I saw the first butterfly of the season, sunning itself on the back of my house beneath the kitchen window. It had just emerged from hibernation and it basked, sensuously opening and closing its purple and gold wings as if inhaling the warmth. Its internal clock, and the warmth, had awakened it. Does time flow more quickly for the butterfly? Do the windows of its compound eyes open onto the same temporal world as my own? Does a sunny spring afternoon stretch for years? Even to me, it seems that time slows down in the spring, as the days grow longer. Time bends and stretches. We imagine that time speeds straight as an arrow, yet sometimes it seems to circle back on itself like watchwork gears. In my garden its toothed wheels mesh with toothed wheels in the heart of the crocuses blooming gold and purple above the muck.

TIME PRESENT

In the flow of time the owl, a symbol of wisdom and memory, is now itself a memory. The point of our rendezvous is past, long past, growing more distant each day. The only thing that hasn't changed is my small monument to our encounter, the three letters on the fence post. But memory also weathers the rush of time and keeps me company, though not such close company as the present. The present, with its corner in the future, is always opening onto something new. The American nineteenth-century poet John Greenleaf Whittier wrote,

> The Present, the Present is all thou hast
> For thy sure possessing;
> Like the patriarch's angel hold it fast
> Till it gives its blessing.

He was referring to the passage from the Old Testament where the patriarch Jacob struggled with an angel at night. For me the owl was like Jacob's angel, and although it would be a stretch to say I wrestled with it in the darkness, our encounter did bestow something wonderful: the knowledge that there are extraordinary beings out there, wild and exotic, making their way in the world, and that my neighbourhood, unremarkable as it may appear, is home to some of them.

But the owl's visit gave me something else as well: an experience of a unique "now," a single bell-note of coincidence that retuned my relationship to the present. And Whittier's quote is essentially about seizing the moment, the only time we *really* have. The payoff of our wrestling match with time is the promise of greater productivity and awareness, the opposite of "wasting time." Whittier's admonishment is a familiar one, though we are such procrastinators and dreamers that living in the present seems almost impossible, a feat for Zen monks and meditating gurus rather than people with careers, children and homes. As Samuel Johnson lamented in *Rasselas*, "No mind is much employed upon the present; recollection and anticipation fill up almost all our moments."

Given that most of us aren't Zen monks, how *do* we embrace, and let ourselves be embraced by, the present? It takes different tacks. Sometimes it arises from boredom—we're often never so much in the present as when we're impatient or bored. Sometimes it ambushes us in the middle of making love . . . we exist nowhere else but in that moment—calm, alert, fully aware. *La petite mort*, as the French call the timeless bliss that comes with orgasm. But this experience is quixotic. And how can we describe "now"? Is it the space between "then" and "next," a tablecloth deftly pulled from beneath the cutlery? Does the present last for an instant, or a millisecond? Or is it only what we make it out to be when we sit still and concentrate on it?

◆ ◆ ◆

It is a moonless city evening. The sounds of neighbours arriving home from work have faded, and darkness has settled. Overhead, a fast-moving, high layer of ribbed cirrus clouds, lit from beneath by the city, looks like phosphorescent X-rays of fossil fish slipping through the stars. The window ledge inside my study is still warm from the afternoon sun, but the sun itself is long gone. Why does the present vanish so quickly? How can there be a seemingly endless series of present moments? It might appear self-evident at first, but "now" isn't what it seems.

The Shape of "Now"

As I write, it is a cool, overcast, late March afternoon in Toronto. Through my study window the featureless sky is pewter grey, and the branches of the leafless trees look like dark coral. What shadows there are appear more like faint stains than black silhouettes. A week ago today was the first official day of spring, and yesterday I saw a couple of robins stalking my slowly greening lawn. But today looks decidedly unspringlike.

Around noon some snow fell, a deluge of large flakes that settled so slowly it seemed as if the air had thickened into a fluid, as if my house were on the floor of some great ocean. The thumbnail-sized crystals filled the sky in a slow-motion cataclysm for a few minutes and then stopped as if they had been a hallucination, leaving only damp spots on the bricks of the pathway that winds through the yard to my garage. Now even those spots have evaporated. In an hour I'll have to dress and leave for a wedding. The bride is an old friend of mine, and it is her second marriage. I wonder what she is thinking right now. As I imagine this, she seems to step into *my* version of "now." But "now" is even bigger than that. It includes the whole earth. Half a world away, in the African bush where it is already night, the Serengeti jackals are on the prowl, keeping a wary eye out for nocturnal lions. In the Antarctic, on the other side of the planet, it is late fall and the sun has stopped rising above the horizon. Knowing how frequently the moon is pelted by small meteorites, I can guess that, at this instant in time, a meteorite the size of a pea is soundlessly striking the surface of Mare Imbrium at 145,000 kilometres per hour. The heat of the impact melts some of the lunar soil into a dark, glassy pit. All this happens in the immensity of "now."

Yet it is also true to say we know that the present moment is very brief—so brief that perhaps it is one-dimensional, maybe even less than a dimension, less than flat. St. Augustine thought so. He likened the present to a knife-edge that separates the past and the future. He said it could not be divided into smaller parts, that it had no extension in time, that "now" was non-dimensional. In other words, it has no depth, no up or down, it simply *is*. Everything in the universe moves along, relatively, at the same speed through time. You can certainly say "the road less travelled," but not "the time less taken." Time, in that sense, is a single path, a tunnel if you like, that we are all crammed into.

The present does seem a vanishingly small place to hold our whole life, and you could say that it really is *all* we have, but at the same time it is bigger than all of us. "Now" holds everything we see. In fact, more than we can see. The present moment is gigantic. We can get a sense of its size from the fact that "now" encompasses the entire planet; we are all joined in a simultaneous instant that spans continents, oceans and mountains. There is a proposal afoot to co-ordinate the operations of the Internet into a single twenty-four-hour day that ignores the world's time zones. If this system is adopted, then the Internet's "universal earth time" will be identical, second by second, to the planetary "now" that also spans the globe at the speed of light.

The Size and Speed of "Now"

Yet "now" also extends beyond our planet. It stretches almost to the moon, which is 1.3 seconds away at the speed of light. But when things get farther away—say, the ninety-three-million-mile distance to the sun—the simultaneous instant ends. How is this possible? We know that light coming from the sun takes eight minutes to get here, so common sense would tell us that that we can easily account for that difference in time, that delay, simply by compensating for it. We can imagine, for example, that the sun could be erupting with a huge solar flare at this very moment, and although it would take eight minutes for us to see the flare, we intuitively think there is a sort of God's-eye view of simultaneity. We know the flare is happening "now"; it's just that we won't see it right away.

But time is not so portable. Although we have an intuitive idea that there is a single present that encompasses the whole universe, physicists and scientists since Einstein have discovered that time is "local." There is no universal "now." As well, in harmony with the relativity principle, time flows at different rates in different areas of the cosmos. Why does distance affect time like this? And what is it that causes time to flow at uneven rates in the various parts of the universe? What could change the tempo of time itself?

Einstein discovered that the closer to the speed of light you travel, the more time slows down. That's why the World War II pilots who walked off the alien spaceship in Steven Spielberg's *Close Encounters of the Third Kind* were the same age as they were when they had been abducted thirty years earlier. That's how speed, and relativity, can affect time. But space also influences time. In the larger universe, sheer distance separates the "now" of various regions. Because of the relative motions of stars and galaxies, and the time it takes light to travel across the universe, we are part of a kind of time medley where everyone has their own "now." Not only that, but gravity affects time as well. Time passes more slowly near the surface of a large planet or star than it does a hundred miles above it. We will revisit this extraordinary fact later, since it turns out that the differential between surface and high-altitude time has a dramatic potential.

Ultimately, it seems that every place in the cosmos exists as a temporal solitude isolated by relativity. Each place's "now" cannot possibly be linked by a simultaneous universal instant that spans the cosmos at once. The only cosmic simultaneity that all parts of the universe can agree on is their distance in time from the birth of the universe. Otherwise it's every region for itself. But these facts are more like diversions or abstractions compared with our day-to-day earthly reality. Although our planet is divided by time zones, for all intents and purposes it exists within a single moment of time. Our definition of "now" does not have to concern itself with the cosmos—at least not yet.

No Time Like the Present

Despite the suppleness of time in the cosmos, each of us knows, viscerally, absolutely, that there is only the present. We cannot travel into the future and change things, nor can we travel into the past and change anything there. We are harnessed to the present moment. Even though we know our memories are real, from the perspective of the present our personal pasts might as well be illusions—we can never go back to revisit them. The past is locked away from us. Our discovery of photography, film and video has made the past more tantalizingly vivid, but no matter how much physical evidence we collect—the photographs on our wall, the souvenirs on our desk—we can't actually touch the past. This is our tragedy, and our liberation. I cannot revisit the night I saw the owl. Yet I will never have to relive my first frightening, exhilarating thunderstorm as a child. In fact, a second ago might as well be a hundred years ago. How eternally reinvented we are! The future is also opaque to us. In a sense we walk backwards into the future and see the present with a kind of peripheral vision.

The twentieth-century philosopher and critic Walter Benjamin has used this image too, comparing the present to an angel who backs into the future while gazing at the past as all the evidence of history piles like wreckage at his feet. "The angel would like to stay, awaken the dead, and make whole what has been smashed. But a storm is blowing in from Paradise; it has got caught in his wings with such violence that the angel can no longer close them. The storm irresistibly propels him into the future to which his back is turned, while the pile of debris before him grows skyward."

So it is with us. Like passengers riding backwards on a train, we see only the landscape we have passed, but nothing ahead of us. Clocks and calendars allow us to measure time, to anticipate events in the future, and this is what gives us a false sense of vista, of being able to meditate on approaching events. We at least have the illusion of facing forward, like someone driving a car who can see objects ahead long before she passes them. We can savour a holiday before it arrives, and the dates pencilled on our calendars—the lunches, graduations and dental appointments—seem to stream towards us like items on a conveyor belt. But that is just an illusion, something that our measurement of time has inculcated in us. We know all too well that the future often arrives as a surprise.

Yet our collective sense of the present, the one we all agree upon, is not the same as our private sense of "now." Our personal sense of time is unique, even though we know that others experience relatively the same flow from future to past, the same simultaneity. Perhaps it might be possible in our individual "now" to actually seize the evanescent border between past and future, and experience time like an elemental force. But even this is difficult. Our personal experience of time shows how elusive the present moment is, the "here and now" that never tarries.

The present is like a needle on a spinning record out of which the past emerges millisecond by millisecond. Only in this case the needle is *making* the record as it plays. It's a magic act, really, like a conjuror pulling endless coloured scarves out of a hat. But the hat is so small it's invisible. There's hardly anything to "now." In fact "now" is so ethereal it is more like a mathematical point. And, it seems, the present is almost infinitely divisible. We keep measuring smaller and smaller units of time in an elusive search for a pure, irreducible "now." The American mathematician David Finkelstein speculates that ultimately there might exist "chronons," indivisible packets of time, like the quantum particles that make up matter, beyond which we will not be able to divide the present moment. At this point, though, the search seems endless. The heart of "now" may well be beyond the grasp of science. If so, and if time can be divided into smaller and smaller units without end, then time is infinite inwards! We only have to speed up our consciousness to experience eternity in a single second.

Touching Time

There is no time like the here and now, as the saying goes, which means something like "seize the moment" or "make hay while the sun shines." But in a stricter, more literal sense, there really *is* no time like the present. "Now" is all we have to work with, and "now" is the only point at which I thought I might be able to touch time itself, experience it anew.

The more I immersed myself in time's paradoxes, the more I got to know its slippery properties. Nothing is more intimate than time, which is inside and outside us, but how can we contact it? As an experiment, I decided to try to experience the flow of time, as if it were something elemental. I would try to feel its current, like a diviner looking for water. I went out into my yard and concentrated as completely as I could on the moment, on feeling the passage of time from second to second. I didn't know how to detect this flow—I didn't even know what I was supposed to feel—but I tried with whatever part of me could feel it, in an act of fierce will.

I had precedents, of course. William James, the famous American psychologist, once attempted something similar. "Let anyone try, I will not say to arrest, but to notice or attend to, the present moment of time. One of the most baffling experiences occurs. Where is it, this present? It has melted in our grasp, fled ere we could touch it, gone in the instant of becoming." Paul Cézanne, the great French painter who had some claim to being the father of modern art, also tried to seize the present and experience it. He wrote, "Right now a moment of time is fleeting by! Capture its reality in paint! To do that we must put all else out of our minds. We must become that moment . . ."

After several days of trying, something happened: I had a fleeting experience of not only the moment, but of the texture of time itself.

TIME WIND

I have a small patch of evergreen broadleaf bamboo growing at the edge of my patio. It's a species of Japanese bamboo that is surviving at the northern limit of its range. The leaves are emerald green and tropical, providing, along with my rhododendron, the only summer foliage in my early spring yard. On the last night of March, a warm wind began blowing out of the south and I went outside to feel the first breath of summer. The night was filled with stars. Jupiter, the calendrical planet of the Mayan timekeepers, glowed brightly at the centre of the southern sky. The breeze was rustling the bamboo leaves, and as the wind swirled up I felt its balmy touch on my skin.

Then, suddenly, it felt as if the wind was blowing deeper than my skin, somehow streaming through me, very gently. This warm current of air was subtly combing through my skin, my muscles, my bones, my very cells. It seemed I could feel it penetrating them all, and I realized that this was what time was, at least for me: a wind that blows through flesh—in fact, through all substance. As quickly as the revelation came over me, the sensation vanished. Once again, exiled from time's touch, I was left looking at the leaves of the bamboo rustling in the night breeze.

Afterwards I wondered if this was entirely my own, unique experience of time, or was it possible that I really had, at least for that brief instant, experienced something profound, something new and intrinsic about time? A few days later I came across these lines in the poem "Song of a Man Who Has Come Through," by D. H. Lawrence: "Not I, not I, but the wind that blows through me! / A fine wind is blowing the new direction of Time." There it was. He too had felt the wind of time. For him, as we learn later in the poem, it was an empty sort of wind, almost sinister, yet ultimately thrilling. He wanted to be carried away by it, to become the new direction of time.

For me, it meant that the flow of time was more ethereal than I had thought, a sort of sandstorm so finely grained that nothing was impervious to it. Time, I realized, could blow through steel and concrete and planets as easily as through empty space. Everything is a sieve to time and time is everywhere. You cannot shut it out. You can lock a diamond in a steel box inside a thousand tons of concrete and time will still blow through that diamond as easily as a breeze through a screen door on a summer afternoon.

The Stealth of Time

One way of experiencing the effects of time without meditating on the present moment, as I did in my yard, is to experience its effects over a relatively short period. We can know it more intimately, perhaps, if we witness the invisible action of time on the world we know the best. As Lucretius wrote in the first century A.D., "No man, we must confess, feels time itself, / But only knows of time from flight or rest of things."

We've probably all seen the effects of time on objects in our home upon returning from a vacation. At first everything is reassuringly the same—the chairs and tables and furniture are clean and just where you left them, a shopping list you made is still on the kitchen table. The fridge is humming peacefully. The drapes are closed, as they were when you left. But there are some changes, evidence of time's infiltration. An apple in a bowl on the counter has withered and become wrinkled. The water in a tumbler beside the bathroom sink has evaporated completely, leaving a graduated series of white rings down the inside of the glass.

It's as if some presence, something no lock or security system could stop from entering, had been in your home while you were away, delicately changing things and going about its subtle business. Most things look the same, but in fact everything has been touched by time's fingers: the varnish on the wooden chairs is a little yellowier, the refrigerator motor is slightly more worn, the foundation of the building itself has settled imperceptibly. In a sense, you haven't come back to the same place. Time's thieves have been there, replacing all your original possessions with slightly altered copies.

So even if time would seem, at least intuitively, to be one of the easiest things to observe, it is still elusive. It may be everywhere, it may touch everything in our homes, and there may be nothing outside of time, nothing that doesn't reflect its passage, yet time remains intangible. Like Lucretius we see only the results of its action, not the thing itself. Time is intimate beyond any intimacy, but untouchable. It is like the wind in the grass.

But there is a deeper sense in which we humans, more than any other living creatures, experience the passage of time. Over the millennia our penchant for technology and abstract thought has helped us to construct an empire of time, a chronological culture within which our lives are scheduled and measured out. Not only do we measure time and use it to regulate our work and creation, we also use it for entertainment and art. Many of the time-based arts, such as music and film, dance with, and within, time. As we'll see further on in this book, we are new sorts of beings on this planet; we are time creatures, and we exist in time unlike anything else alive. There may be older living things, there may be faster metabolisms, but we are masters of time. Time is to our existence as air is to owls, and if we fly at all we fly through time. As Edward Fitzgerald wrote in *The Rubáiyát of Omar Khayyám*, "The Bird of Time has but a little way / To fly—and Lo! the bird is on the wing."

Chapter Two

Time's Arrow

> Time is a great teacher, but unfortunately it kills all its pupils.
> —*Hector Berlioz*

I measure rain by the bucket. Not in the sense of the old saying "It's raining buckets," but literally. Whenever it rains I put a galvanized bucket under the downspout of an eavestrough that drains the small roof over my back stairs. I use the rainwater for my indoor plants. Half a bucket is a decent rain. A full bucket is a downpour, a real drenching. Over the past few days I could have filled the bucket a dozen times.

The first week of April brought not just spring showers but a deluge that went on for days. Rain drummed on my roof at night like a tropical monsoon. Rain poured down the trunk of the maple tree on the front lawn and made little piles of foam where it met the soil. When I drove to the grocery store, rain washed my car cleaner than a car wash. During one downpour the street in front of my house brimmed with water to the curb tops and became a shallow canal that rushed westwards. Robins feasted on drowning worms, and wet, bedraggled squirrels sat glumly on tree branches. Seagulls invaded the neighbourhood, and one morning I heard ducks. Every evening the local news showed pictures of marooned cars and basements with chairs bobbing in thigh-deep water.

One wet afternoon I drove downtown to meet my publisher. Rain had soaked everything. Billboard advertisements were peeling off—a fashion model's forehead had folded over her face. Dark fingers of damp concrete streaked the sides of apartment buildings. In my car the dashboard clock was too misty for me to read the time. I tried to wipe it off but couldn't—the condensation was trapped inside. My chronometer had become a tiny terrarium. Above me, even the clouds pressed closer, as if the weight of the rain had pulled them down from the sky. Low enough that the tops of skyscrapers—including my publisher's— disappeared into them. I parked in a humid underground parking lot, grabbed my umbrella and walked outside.

Water world. Cars sprayed by like motorboats, arcing canopies of water over sidewalks. Umbrellas bobbed everywhere, like glistening tents. They crashed into each other above the crowded sidewalks. The air was warm, though, and a secret, vernal thrill lurked in the lush humidity. When I got to my publisher's, I tapped the rain out of my umbrella in the lobby and took an elevator up into the clouds.

Taking in the view from the windows on the twentieth floor was like looking out of an airplane flying through thick cloud: nothing but a featureless, marine grey tone with a hint of blue-green. I checked my watch and was surprised to see that I was on time, despite my misty automobile timepiece and the many small distractions that had kept me anchored in the present. Outside, the downpour seemed to have washed both past and future away, but here, in the office tower, time ruled again.

My publisher took me to a conference room surrounded on two sides by large plate-glass windows that held back an ocean of fog. The noise and drama of the city were smothered below it; all was ethereal and still. We talked for almost an hour, and afterwards she walked me to the elevator. Through the windows behind her I noticed that the clouds were at last beginning to lift. The elevator doors closed, and I descended back down into the rain. As I drove home, casting my mind forward to what I could make for dinner, a flash lit up the whole sky and turned it a deep electric green. Lightning. The first storm of the year. Thunder was booming when I pulled up in front of my house, and gusts bent the new daffodils in my garden. Jupiter was busy, his chariot rumbling through the clouds.

THE GOD OF TIME

Time is a modern invention. We take time for granted, living inside the minutes, months and years as if they were comfortable clothes. But there was a time before clocks, an era in which the most remarkable aspect of time was not that it could be measured accurately but that it flowed, implacably, in a single direction instead of lingering forever in eternity. This one-way directionality is the tyranny of time, a moving sidewalk we can't step off. But the gods understood that it was both a blessing and a tragedy.

None of the early gods, those of Greece and Rome, had dominion over time except Cronos. Even Jupiter, Cronos's son and the mightiest of all, could not turn back the clock. Although classical scholars differ in their interpretations, down through the ages, Cronos (or Saturn, as the Romans named him) has become popularized as the god of time. Cronos's hair-trigger temper and his sense of regal entitlement seemed to have been passed on to his son, for in Jupiter's rages, which were frequent, he would sometimes hurl lightning bolts to earth.

Cronos features very early in Greek legends. He was born to the first two gods, Uranus and Gaia, who represented heaven and earth respectively. Uranus, deathly afraid of being usurped by his children, confined Cronos and his siblings within Gaia's womb, but she subverted her husband by secretly slipping a sharp-edged sickle to her son Cronos. The next time Uranus "came close," as one legend tactfully put it, Cronos castrated him with the sickle. The blood that spilled from Uranus's wound then formed the Giants and the Furies, while his penis, which had been thrown into the sea, took on a life of its own and eventually transformed into Aphrodite, the goddess of love and beauty.

With his sickle, Cronos ruptured the idyllic eternity where all beings are immortal—a temporal Garden of Eden—and a harsh world governed by time hemorrhaged forth, like the blood from Uranus's emasculating wound. I see this as the mythological beginning of the irreversible flight of time from the past into the future. As Plutarch wrote, "There is Eternity, whence flowed Time, as from a river, into the world." The arrow of time had been loosed.

Cronos, in turn, married and had five children. Because it had been foretold that he would be overthrown by one of his children, just as he had overthrown his father, he swallowed each of them at birth. But, like Gaia before her, Rhea outwitted her husband. By giving Cronos a stone to swallow instead of her newborn son Jupiter, she managed to save at least one of her offspring.

Some have interpreted Cronos eating his children as an allegory about time, which, like a parent, brings them into being but which also outlives and ultimately destroys them. As Ovid observed in his *Metamorphoses*, at the beginning of the first millennium A.D., "Time is the devourer of all things." Writers and artists have flirted with this cannibalistic theme throughout the ages, though none as graphically as Francisco Goya.

There is a famous painting by Goya, completed in 1823, that hangs in the Prado museum in Madrid. Entitled *Saturn Devouring One of His Sons*, it is one of fourteen of Goya's works known as the "black paintings", with which he decorated the interior of his house in Madrid.

The painting is literal, and macabre. Against a nightmarish black background, a naked, bug-eyed Father Time is eating one of his small sons, holding the bloody, headless corpse in his strong hands while tearing off an arm with his teeth. It was in his dining room that, perhaps ironically, Goya chose to hang this disturbing work.

On another level, Goya's interpretation is part of a more recent, sanguinous tradition in our characterization of time. As Aldous Huxley wrote in "Seasons": "Blood of the world, time staunchless flows; / The wound is mortal and is mine." Like Saturn's father, Uranus, we bleed time from the wound of mortality. Like Saturn's children we are sacrificed—that which time creates, time also destroys. But the original Greek myth vied with a philosophical view of time whose characterization was less visceral. Even philosophers of the twentieth century, such as Bertrand Russell, took a more optimistic view of this ancient myth. Echoing Plutarch, he wrote in *A Free Man's Worship and Other Essays*, "A truer image of the world, I think, is obtained by picturing things as entering into the stream of time from an eternal world outside, than from a view which regards time as the devouring tyrant of all that is."

Russell was anticipating the meditative tranquility of modern physicists' notion of a "timescape" in which the past and future commingle. But time's arrow still rules our daily life, and the past seems to press against the back of every second.

Every day, I negotiate between consuming the present—drinking my coffee, savouring it—and being consumed by the tyranny of time. It may not swallow me, but it gnaws away. It says, "In five more minutes you will be late for your class, your students are waiting for you." We flirt and bicker with time like this all day long. As Andrew Marvell wrote, "At my back I always hear / Time's winged chariot hurrying near." In the slam of the car door the moment before we realize the engine is on and the keys are in the ignition, in the moment after we mistakenly press "send all" on a piece of very private email, the deed has already slipped into the past. History owns it now.

Yet Cronos continues to live on. Not only is he the origin of our present-day Father Time, he also gave us the English term for the study of time: horology. The Greeks regarded Cronos as the father of the Horae, the hours. They also regarded him as all-powerful because he presided over the two most important aspects of our existence: the world and the mind. He brought things into being, he aged them and he made them disappear. On top of which, he ruled the intellect. After all, without the ordered flow of time, what could be learned or accomplished? With no "before" or "after," no cause and effect, our mental world would disintegrate into meaninglessness.

Ultimately, Cronos was not the victim of his son's rage, for the Greeks believed that Cronos existed in two forms: his absolute form was eternity and his relative form was time. He always had one foot outside of mortal time. Maybe that's how he evaded Jupiter's final revenge, shuffling the cards of past, present and future in order to escape to Italy, where he remained in exile as the Roman god Saturn. Ultimately, he was a mysterious god. He wasn't physically present in the world. Except for his actions he was unseen. He was also unheard. As William Shakespeare wrote (in a rare tautologous moment) in *All's Well That Ends Well*, "The inaudible and noiseless foot of time."

Over the millennia Cronos was often conflated with Chronos, the Greek personification of time. But Chronos was more an idea than a deity. His name was the source of such time-related words as *chronology*, *chronicle* and *synchronous*. In fact, all the instruments we use to measure time preserve his name: chronometers, for instance, the clocks that ocean-going vessels used to navigate the seas along with sextants before GPS was invented. The aged, sickle-wielding figure of Saturn, as he was portrayed in Roman statues and representations, has also persisted, turning up in editorial cartoons and in New Year's imagery as the slightly pathetic figure of Father Time.

FATHER TIME

He has a long, white beard and always carries the tools of his trade: a scythe and an hourglass. The scythe represents the harvest of the bounty of time (and, by association, death), while the hourglass stands for the ceaseless flow of time (and the measure of how little we have left). This association of Father Time's scythe with death is echoed by another figure, the Grim Reaper, who also brandishes a scythe. In fact, the Reaper, who sometimes carries an hourglass as well, resembles a skeletal version of the more benevolent Father Time. Reflecting his Roman reincarnation as the god of agriculture, Father Time's scythe is said to represent the waxing and waning of the seasons and the regenerative cycle of the crops. Some link the shape of the scythe to the crescent moon. Others say that the scythe represents the flint sickle that Cronos used to castrate his father.

Father Time's old age has long symbolized the wisdom and the unfathomable depths of time. In the modern era, though, he seems to have become, strangely, a slightly buffoonish anachronism. At some point an editorial cartoonist decided to use the image of Father Time to depict the "old year," and since then it has become a standby. In New Year's Day cartoons, the outgoing year slumps away into the past, usurped and humiliated by a baby in diapers that represents the coming year. Any veneration that the classical image of Father Time once generated has been tarnished. Perhaps this modern incarnation of Cronos reflects our belief that Cronos's power over us has diminished. His anachronistic implements, his scythe and hourglass, have been usurped by harvesters and atomic clocks.

The Flow of Time

My next-door neighbour, an older Portuguese man, has a weather vane that he's nailed to a pole in his yard. He and his wife have lived here for years. He tends his fruit trees and vegetable garden according to the seasons; he is attuned to the earth and the cycles of the year. Weather is important to him, as it is to all farmers, and the weather vane, shaped like an arrow, gives him warning by pointing out the direction of the wind. An east wind almost always portends rain. All last week, during the deluge, the arrow pointed east. I like to think of his weather vane as the stationary arrow of time present, pointing into the future as the wind of time flows past. I imagine it without its pole, hovering in the air in mid-flight, like Zeno's Arrow.

◄　◄　◄

Zeno of Elea was born in 488 B.C. in Magna Graecia, a Greek colony in southern Italy. He was adopted and raised by the philosopher Parmenides. Zeno became a philosopher also, and when he came of age he went to Athens with Plato and founded his own school there. Among his students were Socrates and Pericles. During his career he devised a famous paradox, now known simply as "Zeno's Arrow." The paradox involves movement—Zeno used the analogy of an arrow in flight—and one interpretation of his paradox declares that an arrow shot towards a target will never reach it. According to this first interpretation, if an arrow in flight has travelled half the distance to its target, it still has to travel the remaining distance. If you divide the remaining distance in half, the arrow must traverse that distance as well. But what if you kept halving the distance to the target, in smaller and smaller divisions? You end up dividing the remaining space infinitely. If that is the case, declared Zeno, the arrow will never hit its target because it will always have to cross a distance that can be infinitely halved.

Another interpretation of Zeno's paradox is a little subtler, though it ends up having the same bearing on our dilemma. The contemporary philosopher N. A. Routledge explains: "If, says Zeno, everything is either at rest or moving when it occupies space equal to itself, while the object moved is in the instant, the moving arrow is unmoved." It's really more of a mental exercise, I suppose. The first version of the paradox depends on time being infinitely divisible, the second depends on there being "instants" or "nows" in time that are fixed. It all seems very abstract. After all, we know that arrows eventually hit their targets. But Zeno does have a point. He was trying to show how common sense could be confounded by logic, and his paradox serves to ask two questions. Is space infinitely divisible? And is time infinitely divisible as well? We know that physicists keep dividing time into smaller and smaller measurable units, so, in that sense, perhaps time is infinitely divisible. Zeno also suggested that if time were not infinitely divisible, if it were instead made of measurable units like David Finkelstein's "chronons" linked together in a series, then the arrow could be said to be not moving at all when it was temporarily frozen in one of those moments.

◂ ◂ ◂

Certainly Zeno's Arrow is not time's arrow, yet in an important sense they are one and the same. They both reflect the nature of time. But time is a wind that blows from a direction not marked by compasses or wind vanes, neither up nor down nor forth nor back. In fact, according to Paul Davies, the Australian theoretical physicist and science author, our perception of time as flowing like a river is mistaken. Time simply *is*. In his book *About Time*, he explains that contemporary physicists see the universe as a four-dimensional "timescape," where all time—past, present and future—exists at once. But even Davies has to admit that the physicists who study time see a clear bias in it, which they refer to as a "conspicuous asymmetry between past and future directions along the time axis." In other words, objects travelling through time don't seem to be able to move from the future towards the past. In a sadder, more ordinary sense, what's done is done.

This "asymmetry" is most clearly revealed by the second law of thermodynamics, which predicts that disorder increases in a finite universe. A broken wineglass will not reassemble itself. The parking ticket, once written out, cannot be revoked. (Indeed, the parking cop may be the modern embodiment of time's bureaucratic linearity.) And besides, regardless of the abstract and theoretical notions of physicists, our lives are completely ruled by the direction of time's arrow. The inmate on death row does not live in an atemporal "timescape"; for him the clock ticks implacably onwards. And for all of us, the wind of time blows only one way.

Other scientists and philosophers have written about the flow of time as a liquid. Igor D. Novikov, the Russian physicist, called his book *The River of Time*, harking back to Heraclitus's famous dictum that you can never step in the same river twice. Time flows on like water, like the temporary river my street became a few days ago. As the Roman emperor Marcus Aurelius wrote in his *Meditations*, "Time is like a river made up of events, and its current is strong; no sooner does anything appear than it is swept away, and another comes in its place, and will be swept away too." The British poet Matthew Arnold, in his book *The Future*, concurred with Aurelius:

A wanderer is man from his birth.
He was born in a ship
On the breast of the river of Time.

But if we look at time as the physicists do, it makes more sense to think of time as an ocean. We and everything else in the universe float, or bob, in this fluid medium. The present, past and future are merely drifting currents.

Authors have also independently discovered the idea of time as an ocean. In her novel *Marya*, Joyce Carol Oates wrote, "Time is the element in which we exist. . . . We are either borne along by it or drowned in it." Tim Winton, an Australian novelist, offers an extraordinary physical description of time in his recent book of stories called *The Turning*: "Time doesn't click on and on at the stroke. It comes and goes in waves and folds like water; it flutters and sifts like dust, rises, billows, falls back on itself. When a wave breaks, the water is not moving. The swell has travelled great distances but only the energy is moving, not the water. Perhaps time moves through us and not us through it. . . . The past is in us, and not behind us. Things are never over."

The Inner Timescape

Things are never over. Could it be that we each exist in our own private timescape, in which the past surges through us? Sometimes it flows silently, unseen and unfelt. Other times we become aware of this buried current animating our lives.

Two mornings ago there was a break in the rain. The sun shone through the clouds, so I sat out on my patio to have a coffee after breakfast. It was a meditative moment, and as I surveyed the yard my mind's eye turned inward. When it did, it seemed to ricochet all over time—past, present and future. Sipping my coffee and looking at the bamboo leaves reminded me of a vacation I took years ago, the way the coconut palms shone like green vinyl in the bright sunlight. Then the phone rang and I was right back in the present moment. It was a friend. She was making plans for a dinner party on the weekend, could I attend? I went inside and looked at my calendar and realized that yes, I would be free that night. The buzzer of my toaster oven interrupted our conversation. A croissant I'd put in to warm ten minutes earlier was now ready, like a time capsule from myself. Without missing a beat, I went from past to present to future and back again. I was free, at least in my mind, to go anywhere within my personal timescape at will.

It is our ability to time-travel like this, within our minds, that makes us the creatures we are. Without this ability there would be no art, no dreams, no cities or buildings. Everything we have accomplished began as an imagining set in a hoped-for future. The Parthenon was once an inkling in Pericles's imagination. Yet at the same time we are the inheritors of a grand history, and an even grander prehistory. These have provided us with the resources and the prototypes upon which to build our "now." History is the podium of the present.

A Ghost Creek

It was as if the spirits of the rain were fleeing the earth, smoked out by the first sun in days. "*Après le déluge*," as Rimbaud put it. The wet lawns and pavement and gardens and houses steamed in the hot April sunlight. I came out to look at the spectacle. Eddies of mist curled languorously up roofs and into the sky. Shreds of fog were caught like wispy cotton in tree branches. A remarkable silence amplified small noises—water dripping from an overflowing eavestrough, the song of a migratory warbler in someone's yard. The sun poured through the gossamer architecture of the pillars of mist as if through a cathedral window.

Across the street I saw my neighbour George, standing like an icon in front of his white clapboard house, staring at his yard. I often saw him there, tending his perfect lawn or clipping his juniper bushes. During a conversation a year before, he had told me that he had lived his whole life within the same three blocks. He was born more than eighty years ago "one street over" and had lived in various nearby apartments and houses for almost a century. Time had congealed in his person, though he was still strong and tall and unstooped.

I called out hello and George waved and walked across the street towards me. He was wearing a blue nylon jacket and a baseball cap. With his close-cropped white hair and all-weather tan he looked like the groundskeeper for an exclusive golf course. We watched the mist rise and talked about the recent rains. George asked if my basement was wet and I told him no, fortunately, it was completely dry. He said that the house next to his had a wet basement, and so did the house two doors down from me. "Over the years," he said, "I heard about other wet basements and realized that they're all connected in a line. A meandering line." He gestured. "Must be the path of an old creek they filled in to build this neighborhood."

We talked some more and then he went back to meditating on his lawn while I walked around my house into the backyard. It was mid-afternoon, and my mist-enshrouded lawn glowed emerald in the sunlight. I looked down the row of neighbours' yards to the east and noticed that the buds on the trees were beginning to swell. Then I imagined what it might have looked like 120 years ago, before there were any houses. I imagined the small creek high with rainwater, the green bulrushes and willows and cedar growing along its banks. A great blue heron stilting the shallows.

A river is more like a living thing than a cliff is, or a valley. It moves and changes and adapts. And from what George told me, it seems that even a river that has been filled in for a hundred years still has a soul, a slim, insistent thread of linked water molecules that continues to flow towards the lake. Here in the present, that lost, unnamed stream is more like a ghost creek that lingers underground. It is like time past, silently flowing through our lives even when we can't detect it. The only evidence of its existence is a string of wet basements. My house must have been close to the bank of that extinct creek.

I began to think about how to resurrect the creek. I could hand-deliver flyers that would convince my neighbours to join in my project, the world's first reconstitution of a lost creek. I went through my arguments. I decided I would target the neighbours with wet basements first. If we gave the river a course, I would argue, if, instead of fighting it, we acknowledged it, perhaps we'd be able to dry their basements out. Then I would explain my plan.

We would let the creek run through a special series of underground conduits, an interconnected system of glass pipes and sealed basement aquariums. Once the flow had been re-established, we could restock it with a limited but viable ecology of small fish and underwater plants. It would be a fine diversion, on a midwinter's night, to watch minnow-sized sticklebacks building their little stone nests in a basement aquarium under artificial light or to watch a dragonfly larva drift with the slow current through one side of the basement and out the other.

A crimson cardinal landed in my magnolia tree and startled me out of my reverie with his swooping, ricocheting call. I realized that this erstwhile creek will probably never run again. It struck me as a dubious engineering accomplishment—we stop up rivers that have flowed for thousands of years in order to fill them in and extirpate them for all time, burying any evidence of their existence under buildings and concrete. I thought about my plan to reconstitute the ghost creek and realized that the plan itself, the idea of it, was already acquiring a history and moving into the past.

How quickly the present slips into history.

Even my thoughts have a past, even my thoughts cleave to time's arrow. Or do they? Isn't the ghost creek alive in my imagination? There is a second world, the past animated by memory, that lives in my mind. With my inner eye, I can see every brick of my house, the shape of every boulder of ornamental limestone in my garden, the leathery green leaves of my rhododendrons. I can walk to the virtual garage, open the virtual door and get into my car. I can revisit the garage as it looked after last year's blizzard, the snow piled on the roof, the delicate etchings of frost on the inside of the windows.

I can move in and out of the flow of time at will. And this is how I, we, keep from being marooned in the present, locked into time's one-way flow. Our memory and imagination allow us to reconstitute the past, to resurrect it, to point time's arrow in any direction we please. The only place in the universe immune to time's tyranny is our mind. That is how we escape being devoured by time. We can see the world from almost any viewpoint, we can imagine what it is like to be an eagle or a dolphin or a bat or a butterfly. We can even become time itself. As Jorge Luis Borges wrote in his essay "A New Refutation of Time," "Time is the substance from which I am made. Time is a river which carries me along, but I am the river; it is a tiger that devours me, but I am the tiger; it is a fire that consumes me, but I am the fire." Our mortal triumph is our ability to escape time's arrow. We are chrononauts who swim through time in any and all directions and are thus unlike anything else on the planet.

Chapter Three

Monks, Steamboats and Femtonians: Measuring Time

> Confound him, too,
> Who in this place set up a sundial,
> To cut and hack my days so wretchedly
> Into small portions
> —*Titus Maccius Plautus* (c. 254–184 B.C.)

Any day now the leaves will open. April is almost over, and the twigs on the horse chestnut tree on my neighbour's lawn look like bronze sceptres—a fat, shiny bud crowning each tip. Every morning I walk to the corner grocery store on some concocted errand—milk, oranges, cheese, anything I can think of—in order to scan the maple trees in my neighbourhood. Their yellow-green flowers have already opened, and from a distance their crowns are misty chartreuse. But the leaves are not out yet, though I know that once the flowers open, the leaves can't be far behind. Each floret is like the ripcord on a tiny parachute; once pulled, a leaf will blossom out after it. So I shade my eyes from the spring sun and search for the first green leaves.

For the past few decades I have marked down the exact day the leaves emerged. Last year it was April 29. The year before, it was May 7. The earliest, since I've been keeping track, was April 14. The latest was

May 8. It's always a bit of a roller-coaster ride; winter relinquishes spring unwillingly, it holds on. If a cold front arrives, the entire leaf-opening spectacle is delayed, sometimes for weeks. Forsythia bushes are suspended in perpetual yellow bloom like flowers in a florist's cooler; magnolia blossoms can be transfixed for two weeks.

Two years ago, when the leaves opened late, I became impatient. I had an impulse to drive south to meet the advancing wave of spring. It was stalled somewhere and I wanted to get to it. About a decade before, I had raced the springtide from Miami to Toronto in an Oldsmobile. It was late February but spring was well underway in southern Georgia, warm enough for me to sleep in the car at a pull-off with the windows rolled down. Outside the car, the leaves had already opened and the night air was filled with the sound of trilling frogs. It felt more like late May in Toronto. The next day I had a slice of homemade pecan pie for breakfast and then continued north, through Georgia and Tennessee, turning back the calendar of spring from May to April to March. As I drove through the southern Appalachian mountains, banded with pink and blue limestone strata like layer cakes, I noticed the thinning of spring's greenery and by the time I reached Kentucky the buds had only just begun to swell on the trees, while snow still nestled in the roadside hollows. I spent the night at a motel in coal country. The next morning dawned cold, and midway through Ohio snow began to fall. By the time I reached the Canadian border a blizzard was in progress. I'd left summer a thousand miles behind me.

Years

The shock wave of spring spreads northwards at sixteen miles a day, a little more than half a mile an hour. You could easily outwalk spring; it takes months to get from Miami to Toronto. Spring's advance is really the tilt of the earth—fifteen degrees—translated into movement as our planet circles the sun. Starting in late December and accelerating after March 21, the northern hemisphere of the earth begins tipping towards the sun like a sun worshipper on a beach. The sun rises a little higher in the sky each day, pulling the tide of spring behind it like the wedding train of Venus. It's so dependable you could set your watch by it.

Even without a calendar to guide me I know that my "leaf clock" is accurate to within three weeks, at least for Toronto. I'm like the early humans who had no calendars or clocks. They looked for signs: the arrival or departure of migratory birds, the blooming or seeding of plants. And there's a lot of redundancy in the natural calendar—it's no problem when the signs are delayed. Here in Toronto if the night-hawks are late, the fiddlehead ferns will still unfurl like clockwork. If there's a cold snap that delays the leaf opening by a week or two, the first swallowtail butterfly will always be on schedule some warm May afternoon. These are backups.

The sun is more precise. If I jam a piece of wood in a crevice on a large, flat rock so tightly that even winter storms can't budge it, I've built a solar observatory. I can use it to measure the length of the noon-hour shadow and mark it out with scratches on the rock throughout the year. Although the distance between one day and the next is minimal, if I wait for twenty-nine days, one lunar cycle, there is a measurable difference where the noon shadow of the stick ends. This is the beginning of astronomy. Every summer solstice the shadow will land in exactly the same place. From here it is a hop to Stonehenge, Egyptian pyramids and Galileo. But I'm getting ahead of myself. A year is easy to measure by this method, even in the tropics, where eternity lingers in the seasonless months.

Months, Weeks, Days and Hours

Yesterday, the first of May, the leaves opened. It was hot in the afternoon, and everyone seemed to be out walking—young mothers with rubber-wheeled strollers, kids on noisy skateboards and old couples walking arm in arm. The warm wind had a buoyancy to it, a softness tempered by the moist air, and it felt as if the whole city had been secretly towed overnight to the Caribbean. I spent the afternoon weeding and resetting the frost-jumbled bricks that divide my garden from the lawn. I also took my outdoor table and chairs out of the garage, wiped off the winter grit and set them up on the patio. It was good to be out in the sun.

The evening continued warm, and after sunset I sat out with a glass of wine to toast the moonrise over the newly solidifying crowns of the trees. It was a waning moon that rose late like a big, lopsided orange into the warm embrace of a May night. It orbited low in the sky the way a summer moon does, and its skin shimmered with a faded chiaroscuro of dark craters and pale deserts. The moon's disc was surrounded by a faint yellow corona, tinged at the edges with green. Although waning, it was still bright enough to lay shadows across my back lawn. I had to remind myself that moonlight was second-hand, that it reflected off lunar geography and travelled through airless desolation to reach me. No wonder it seemed to hypnotize what it touched. The moon that night was like an elliptical map of crumbling, empty civilizations, a fossil cameo lighting a sky that seemed almost green. Leaf green.

There were so many new leaves opening in the darkness you could almost hear them unfurling. The night was filled with chlorophyll, soaked in a deep, nocturnal emerald, and the warm air was perfumed with the fresh scent of millions of new leaves. Their raw, primal verdancy, the delicate and immeasurable power of their growth, saturated the twilight. Millions of leaves were hatching like green butterflies from their chrysalis buds, their wings unfolding into leaves. When the next full moon ascends, those leaves will have reached full size—the shape they'll hold all summer.

If I made a record of each full moon by scratching a circle above the noon scratch on my rudimentary solar calendar, I'd discover that there were about twelve full moons in a year. It's a natural way to divide the year, and very early in our history, years were recognized to have twelve months. Alexander Marshak, an anthropologist who specializes in the interpretation of ancient artifacts, has deciphered what he believes to be the first lunar calendar. Discovered in 1960 in Uganda, it is a twenty-thousand-year-old piece of carved bone with a series of lines incised into it. If Marshak is right, this stone-age artifact (called the Ishango bone) pre-dates the earliest confirmed lunar calendar—on a Babylonian clay tablet from 750 B.C.—by seventeen thousand years.

Lunar phases, whenever they began to be observed, provided the first monthly calendar for humans, and several religions, notably Judaism and Islam, still base the timing of their observances on the lunar cycle. Of the two, Islam is arguably the most strictly lunar; all of Islam's important religious observances begin only when a cleric has made the first visual sighting of the moon's crescent.

Today, regardless of the religious and sacred associations, calendars are largely secular, and very practical. They measure months, weeks and days in a gradated scale of chronometric precision, from coarse to fine, that allows us to plan our lives. A calendar is a bit like predicting the future. Which could be why the superstition arose that it's bad luck to look ahead in a calendar, although anyone who believes this must not get much done, because a calendar is the most basic of day-planners. And days are the most natural division of time. The circadian rhythm of night and day shaped the earliest origins of life and is the basic pulse of our existence. Weeks, instead, are much more abstract.

By 400 B.C. the Greeks were unique amongst their fellow civilizations in following a planetary week, in which a different planet—the Sun, Mercury, Venus, the Moon, Mars, Jupiter and Saturn—ruled each of the seven days. When Alexander the Great conquered Asia between 323 and 336 B.C., he brought this system to Egypt, where it caught on. It's with us still, in both French and English, though more obviously in French. The English week has Saturday (Saturn's day) and Sunday (the Sun's day), but Francophones have *lundi* (the Moon's day), *mardi* (Mars), *mercredi* (Mercury), *vendredi* (Venus) and a remnant of Jupiter in *jeudi*.

Most other civilizations around the Mediterranean continued to follow an eight-day, or *nundinum*, cycle for centuries afterwards, although, for their own reasons, the Jews also observed a seven-day week. These inconsistent calendars remained unchanged for millennia, until the rise of the Roman Empire. Rome had inherited an eight-day *nundinum* from the Etruscans, but as their empire grew they were eventually exposed to the Egyptian system. Rome had always had a soft spot for mystery cults and practices originating in the Middle East, particularly if they came from Egypt. And the Egyptian association of individual gods with particular days was just too much to resist. The curious thing is that the seven-day week hadn't already arrived in Rome along with everything else Hellenistic—Roman culture was 90 percent Greek, after all. But for some reason the seven-day week had to be exported from Greece to Egypt and then to Rome. The Roman adoption of the seven-day week came gradually, between 50 B.C. and A.D. 30. By A.D. 79, the year of the eruption of Vesuvius, it had been instituted throughout most of the Roman Empire.

The seven-day week was also a better fit with the lunar month, dividing more evenly into the twenty-nine-day cycle. Lunar months had always posed a problem for calendar makers. Early on, probably about 3,500 years ago, the Babylonians found that the solar year gradually got out of harmony with the lunar year. They calculated that by adding a day to their lunar month, changing the number of days in a year from 348 to 360, their calendars would agree more correctly with the length of the solar year. But eventually even this system got out of synchronization, so they devised a new, complicated method that changed the number of days in a year to as few as 353 and as many as 385.

The Egyptians adopted the Babylonian calendar early, probably by 3,000 B.C., though they simplified it by abandoning the lunar months altogether and instituting a 365-day calendar based on the flood patterns of the Nile River. Each month had thirty days, and at the end of every year, five additional days were added. This was the system that was passed on to the Romans. The Romans, however, soon noticed troubling minor discrepancies between the Egyptian calendar and the solar year, and it became Julius Caesar's obsession to devise a perfect calendar. The calendar he created is essentially the one in use today throughout the world, though it was fine-tuned slightly by Pope Gregory XIII in 1582 and as a result is now called the Gregorian calendar. But how did the Egyptians come up with hours, and why are there twenty-four of them in a day? Lunar months are a natural division, as are years and days. Hours, on the other hand, have a slightly more ambiguous and numerological pedigree.

The number twelve held a mystical significance for the Egyptians. It was probably because the year divided naturally into twelve lunar months that the priests of Ra likewise decreed that day and night would each be divided into twelve hours. But these "hours" were not of equal length. At the time of the winter solstice in Alexandria, the night lasts fourteen hours and the day ten hours, making an hour of night seventy minutes long and an hour of day only fifty minutes long. The Egyptians probably guessed this, but without clocks there was no way for the hours to be accurately measured. By 1600 B.C. both Egypt and Babylon had clepsydras, or water clocks, that used water dripping from one measured container into another to determine equal lengths of time. The trouble was that the clocks were finicky and temperature-sensitive; when the water cooled at night, "time" would flow twice as fast. Still, the twenty-four-hour day prevailed and ultimately became the world standard. Yet the division of hours into minutes had to wait for thousands more years after the Egyptians.

In some sense, even with all my clocks—the digital clock on my stove, my analogue watch and my various wall clocks—the passage of the hours strikes me as mysterious. Clock time seems abstract and disconnected from my own experience of continuous time—the rising of the moon, the setting stars. As François Rabelais wrote, "I never follow the clock: hours were made for man, not man for hours."

This morning, on my own time, I opened the blinds onto a new world—an empire of green. My house was flooded with emerald light. Overnight, in the moonlight, the trees had transformed from bud-misted scaffolds into leafy landscapes. Summer was underway, and the boughs of the trees were restless in the breezy morning air, alive with their new weight of life. A new season had begun, and I felt a slight poignancy. But there is nothing sentimental about this lushness; it means business. We measure our years by seasons, and with each successive year those seasons are more deeply marked by the memories of seasons past. And the seasons unspool the story of our lives.

MINUTES

> I stood on the bridge at midnight,
> As the clocks were striking the hour.
> —*Henry Wadsworth Longfellow*

Clocks have been with us for about seven hundred years, since the late thirteenth century. There is some evidence that the Chinese constructed one almost six hundred years before that, but for one reason or another they abandoned the technology, leaving it for the Europeans to reinvent. It seems strange that the Dark Ages, which stretched from the end of the Roman Empire in A.D. 450 to the beginning of the high Middle Ages in A.D. 1100, hatched the technology of time measurement, but it did. This was partially because of the rise of monasticism. Clocks, along with Anno Domini (A.D., in the year of our Lord), we owe to Christianity.

Monasteries not only kept the flame of civilization lit by translating Greek and Roman texts, they also provided the kind of stable, scholastic environment that fostered technical innovation. Cloistered monks needed an accurate way to schedule their many daily prayers, and this called for a fail-safe method of timing. At first they used calibrated candles, hourglasses and sundials, but all of these had limitations. It was the mechanics of devotion, for keeping an appointment with the divine, that propelled the evolution of their timekeeping devices. After all, the heavenly realm had its own schedule, one that transcended the vagaries of seasonal changes in the length of day and night. As early as the eleventh century, monasteries had built mechanical devices attached to bells that announced prayer time, and it was these machines, or at least the concept behind them, that provided the basis for the invention of the clock. Clocks, at their very inception, already had one cog in the otherwordly.

It was no accident, then, that the first true mechanical clock was installed at Dunstable Priory in Bedfordshire, England, in A.D. 1283. Twelve years earlier, a key component, something called the "escapement," had been designed by a technician known to history only as Robert the Englishman. The escapement was a clever invention that used toothed wheels, counterweights and drive-gears to convert the downward force exerted by gravity on a drive weight into a regular mechanical movement. Within a decade the escapement, and the clocks that it powered, had spread across Europe. Large public clock towers were erected in many European cities. At first a great number of them had no clock faces and only sounded bells on the hour. It took a few more decades until the first dials, with a single hand to mark the hours, appeared.

Public clocks must have seemed exceptionally modern at the time. They were the first mechanical technology to surpass Rome's, and the first sign that the Middle Ages were beginning to draw to a close. A public clock tower with a dial face marking the hours was a radical innovation, not just because time itself had become magically visible, but also because all those who heard its bells could co-ordinate their daily activities. Shops and markets began to keep regular hours; appointments could be co-ordinated for anyone within earshot.

Tourists travelled in from the country just to stand and stare at these marvels, particularly the most advanced ones, which had dials embraced by scrolled brackets and carved figures that held the clock face like a votive object. But no matter how clocks were dressed up in classical ornamentation, nothing could conceal the austere, geometric modernity of the clock face itself—a window into time. It must have been an extraordinary period, particularly for the wealthy, who could afford to have smaller, personal clocks built for domestic use, much like the first personal computers of the 1980s. We take clock dials for granted now. They even look a bit quaint beside an LCD digital time display, but they still have a decided modernity to them.

The clock face was a practical solution to the problem of representing the passage of twenty-four hours compactly and simply. All previous timepieces had relied on a linear and often interrupted operation—hourglasses had to be turned upside down when they ran out, clepsydras had to be refilled and maintained at a constant temperature, calibrated candle clocks simply burned down, and sundials could only tell time when the sun was out. The mechanical clock was new, it had its own source of energy. It was independent, almost alive. It was as if a portion of the great river of time had been diverted into a minor eddy, confined and harnessed within the clockwork gears and cogs of the timepiece. Inevitably, those same gears would quantify human lives themselves.

◂ ◂ ◂

Above my desk I have a digital, Olympic-style time clock that measures not just hours, minutes and seconds, but tenths and even hundredths of seconds. I use it like a chronometric mascot to spur me on; according to it, time isn't just passing, it's flying. The clock's face is a sliding spectrum of time, from coarse to fine. On the left the unmoving hours are posted like newspaper headlines. Next comes the stately procession of minutes, then the seconds ticking by. To the right are the tenths of seconds. They pass by distressingly fast. But it is the hundredths of seconds that I find fascinating. They're hypnotic, like a waterfall or a light show. They dance furiously, flashing by so quickly I can't read them. Most wall clocks advance stealthily, almost imperceptibly, but this one gushes. My Olympic clock constantly reminds me that my leisurely perspective on time is an illusion.

In another sense, though, my sports timer confirms the twofold accuracy of a much earlier chronometer: the hourglass. Although an hourglass cannot measure an accurate second, it can gauge a fairly accurate minute and get close to measuring an exact hour. Yet there is something even more exact about it. An hourglass is a perfect functional symbol; it both symbolizes time and measures it. The sand rushes through the present moment, the waist of the hourglass, on its way to the past, the heap of sand at the bottom, in a rushing, dry waterfall. The resemblance between my sports clock and the hourglass deepens here. Just as hundredths of seconds flow faster than tenths of seconds, the speed of the falling sand is faster in the centre of the flow than at the edges, where it is slowed by its contact with the glass. The speed of "now," in both chronometers, seems infinitely divisible into ever-faster increments.

There is a further parallel, not with my sports clock, but between the hourglass and time. Beyond the hourglass's direct representation of time's flow is the correspondence between the shape of the hourglass and the division of time into past, present and future. The reservoirs of future and past, the upper and lower bulbs respectively, are connected by the waist of the present. Perhaps the present moment, our "now," is more exactly like the waist of the hourglass than we know. "Now" is unmoving, and instead, time rushes through it, giving us the illusory sense that the present moment races from the past towards the future, or that the future flows through it towards the past. Maybe the present moment is more like the lens of a projector that the film of time is playing through.

The hourglass has a final deep parallel with time. If, at the end of time, time reverses and the universe runs backwards, as an astophysicist named Thomas Gold has proposed, then turning the hourglass upside down after the "future" has run out is a perfect allegory. Perhaps the process repeats endlessly, the universe inverting like an egg timer in a kitchen morning after morning, or like the demon that Nietzsche wrote about (who, like Thomas Gold, we will encounter later on in this book). Finally, there is the analogy between mortality and time running out. The Grim Reaper doesn't brandish his hourglass idly.

◆ ◆ ◆

Mechanical clocks had, and still have, an element of mortality to them. Their measured ticks seem to dole out our lives. I remember how, when my mother was in her final days, she would keep glancing at her bedside clock. It was her compass, an absolute within the delerium that slowly overtook her. It was also a solace of sorts. I think the last control she could exercise over the world was to keep track of her daily calendar of events, of impending visits by her home-care nurse and the lonely hours of the night. Clocks are not the enemy, of course. They only measure our mortality. (Though neither are they our friend.) But the connection between clocks and mortality is strong nonetheless. It sometimes seems as if time stalks us, like the ticking clock in the stomach of the crocodile in *Peter Pan*.

I doubt that associations of mortality were a factor when clocks were a brand-new technology, when the chiming of the hours became a theme song to the cultural awakening of Europe in the sixteenth century. Still, the measurement of minutes was centuries away. Although the church had already instituted St. Bede the Venerable's division of the hour into sixty minutes and the minute into sixty seconds, at least on paper, it wasn't until Christiaan Huygens invented the pendulum clock in 1665 that accurate minutes became a reality and Bede's abstractions became practicable. Huygens, the son of the famous Dutch poet Constantijn Huygens, was a mathematician, physicist and astronomer. His invention of the pendulum clock was more of a practical necessity than an end in itself; he wanted to measure the motion of the planets and their moons as precisely as possible. Eleven years later Ole Römer used Huygens' pendulum to calibrate the occlusion of the moons of Jupiter and came up with the first quantitative estimate of the speed of light: 136,000 miles per second, which although 26 percent lower than the currently accepted speed, was nonetheless very close. It was to be another half-century after Huygens' pendulum that clocks could measure seconds with any precision.

Seconds

> Your average day of 1,440 minutes consists of 86,400
> seconds. If the average thirty-day month, then, has 2,592,000
> seconds and hence the average year consisting of twelve
> thirty-day months would consist thereby of 31,104,000
> seconds, I have then, in fact, lived (since I am approaching
> my thirty-sixth year) but 1,088,640,000 seconds.
> —*Glenn Gould*

When I was a child our family camped every summer in the wilds of northern Ontario. They were idyllic months, canoeing by day and setting up camp in the late afternoon, on an island in the middle of a lake to avoid the mosquitoes that were thicker on the mainland shores. Most of these lakes were so pure you could dip your cup in them and drink. The weather was usually sunny, but on hot afternoons, convection storms would build and cruise over the landscape—brooding cloud-towers with lightning at their bases. Inevitably there were occasional night storms, some of which were terrifically violent. A sleeping bag and a canvas tent don't feel like much protection in a severe lightning storm, and my father, to allay my fears, taught me how to calculate how far away the storm was by timing the thunderclaps. You just count the seconds between flash and thunder. Five seconds equalled a mile. For "seconds" we counted out "steamboats," stopping as soon as we heard the thunder.

Sometimes the storm would miss us, never getting closer than four steamboats, but more often the storm would score almost a direct hit. It was hard to concentrate on counting when the tent was flapping in the wind and the rain drummed down so hard that it sounded like the campsite was being washed away. It was even more difficult to concentrate when there was no delay between the brilliant violet flash of lightning and the bedrock-shaking explosion of thunder. But as the first steamboats began to emerge between the flashes and the thunder, I knew, to my relief, that the storm was finally leaving.

Years later I discovered that not only could you tell how far away the lightning was, you could also, using the same method, map out the lightning branches, particularly the horizontal ones that run parallel to the ground. Now when I hear thunder begin, especially the low, rippling thunder from deep in the clouds, I start counting, and by timing the length of the thunder's peal I can calculate the length of the lightning branch. Sometimes they are more than a mile long. Using time to measure phenomena is precisely why accurate timepieces became a necessity, and why the second, something that is now so ubiquitous in our vocabulary and experience, was also necessary to quantify.

It turned out that the relationship between time and space, or in this case time zones and longitude, became the incentive to begin measuring precise seconds, and it fell to a carpenter from Yorkshire named John Harrison to devise a clock that could measure them. By the early eighteenth century, Britain was a maritime superpower in command of thousands of oceangoing ships. The difficulty of determining accurate position at sea was one of the greatest dilemmas facing the nation. Faulty navigation led to the loss of ships, lives and valuable cargo, and as more and more ships plied the sea, the losses mounted. It took the great maritime disaster of 1707 to galvanize England into action. Four Royal Navy ships sailed off course near the coast of the Scilly Isles and ran aground, costing the lives of fourteen hundred sailors. In an act of Parliament in 1714 Britain offered a price of £20,000 (equivalent to US $7 million today) to anyone who could accurately calculate longitude at sea.

Determining latitude had always been easy for sailors. By measuring the angle of the Pole Star and referring to an almanac of sun and star positions, they could judge their latitude exactly. But longitude posed another problem. To measure that you had to have an accurate clock, because you had to subtract your local time from the time at the prime meridian, which runs through Greenwich. A reckoning accurate within a minute would give you your position to within a mile. But there were no clocks capable of doing this at sea, since the wave-induced rolling motion of boats stymied their workings. It was such a long-standing problem that many ships' navigators simply sailed due south until they reached the correct latitude, then sailed due west or east. Needless to say these were not direct routes.

John Harrison took up the challenge, not just because of the extraordinary prize but also to save lives. He laboured for twenty-seven years, building successively more accurate clocks until his crowning achievement: the No. 4 Chronometer, which was tested on a voyage between Britain and Jamaica in 1761. It was able to maintain its accuracy during the entire voyage. He won the prize.

As a practical monument to his achievement, the Greenwich Observatory in England installed its famous time ball at the top of a tower visible to all boats in the adjacent harbour. When the ball dropped, it marked the precise hour, and maritime navigators would synchronize their ship's clock with the Greenwich master clock. Knowing where you were depended on knowing what time it was.

Milliseconds, Nanoseconds and Coastlines

> The clock, not the steam-engine, is the key machine of the
> modern industrial age.
> —*Lewis Mumford*

Imagine that you have been hired to measure a small nation's coastline. It's a big job, but you have enthusiastic assistant surveyors, an unlimited budget and a whole summer ahead of you. You begin the survey one sunny May morning at the southernmost point of the coast, right at the border. The guards on the other side wave to you, and seagulls cry as they hover on a brisk, onshore breeze. The ocean is deep blue and dotted with whitecaps. North of you is a long, white beach. You begin your work.

The beach is relatively straight and quick to measure. It turns out to be almost two miles long. You break for an early lunch. The survey crew is talkative and excited. You decide that one summer should be ample time to measure the whole shoreline.

After lunch you begin to survey the point that shelters the beach's north end. Here you realize that you will have to simplify your measurements. Instead of measuring the gradual curve of the point, you take a series of locations around it and measure the distance between them. It's sort of cheating, but then again, how far off the actual distance could it be? Probably not a significant amount. Measuring the point takes up the early part of the afternoon, and as you and your crew come around to the other side, you see that the shoreline extending north is nowhere near as straight as the beach you measured in the morning. It is a long series of successive points, bays and inlets, some large, some small.

The first bay is simple, though it contains a small point that, after a brief conference, you and your assistants elect not to measure. "It's too small," you say. The next point has a little bay in it, perhaps only twenty feet across. If you measure the bay, it will extend the length of the shoreline by almost a hundred feet. But a decision has to be made. In the end you decide that all smaller features will be ignored. If you begin to measure every little bay and inlet, the job might take all year.

When you've finished for the day, you and your crew set up camp on the beach. After dinner, under the stars and around a driftwood fire, everyone talks about the day's work. The conversation is lively and friendly at first, but then the discussion turns into an argument. One of the surveyors, a philosophy student, insists that the survey has to be done as conscientiously as possible. She didn't like the decision to skip smaller features. "Every little bay and inlet has to be measured," she insists. "There is an absolute length to the shoreline, and we're being paid to measure it."

"Hold on," says the lead surveyor. He has a degree in mathematics and works for the department of national cartography. "Where do we stop? Let's say we measure a small bay and it comes to forty-five feet. But what if there's a big boulder embedded on the shore of this bay? We measure it and it adds another five feet. Do we include that?"

"Why not?" asks the philosophy student.

"Okay," says the lead surveyor. "What if there's an indentation in that boulder, a crack that measures a foot and a half on each side. Do we include those three feet?"

"Why not?" the philosophy student asks again.

"All right," says the lead surveyor. "What if, in that crevice, there were a smaller crevice? Would we measure that?"

The philosophy student realizes where this is going.

"You've got me there," she says. "Obviously there is no end."

"That's right," says the lead surveyor. "If you measure ever smaller features on a shoreline, going from feet to inches to hundreths of an inch, you'll soon discover that this nation's coastline is infinitely long!"

◆ ◆ ◆

Our little survey crew stumbled on a fact that has a profound implication for measuring time. One of the paradoxes of Zeno's Arrow was that it could never reach its target because the distance it had to travel could be infinitely halved. Nearly three thousand years later, in the early half of the twentieth century, a British scientist by the name of Lewis F. Richardson continued Zeno's quest. Coastlines and borders fascinated Richardson. Visiting countries that shared a common, zigzagging border, such as Holland and Belgium or Spain and Portugal, he found that the encyclopedias in each of these countries had estimates of their common borders that varied by as much as 20 percent. The discrepancy could be blamed on bad surveying, but Richardson didn't think so. He thought there was something more profound going on, and he was right. But it wasn't until years later that the French mathematician and physicist Benoît Mandelbrot, the father of chaos theory, picked up on Richardson's interest in borders and coastlines and took it to its logical conclusion. Like our imaginary surveyors, he discovered that any irregular, natural coastline is endless.

You'd think that there would be a limit to this measurement. After all, coastlines exist in the real world. They are fixed, measurable. They don't wiggle around or fade in and out of existence. But Mandelbrot discovered otherwise. Certainly if you were measuring something like a perfect rectangle lying on the ground, there would be a final value, an ultimate, fixed distance, but he found that with an irregular, natural shoreline there was no end to the bays and peninsulas. They simply got smaller and smaller until finally you were measuring them on the molecular and then the atomic scale. Perhaps on the atomic scale there might be an end to the measurement, a final length of the coastline. But that's where, maddeningly, everything becomes fuzzy, because the quantum world is indeterminate.

Time, it appears, is the same. Like a shoreline, time is composed of ever smaller, divisible units of itself. A second then, at least hypothetically, ought to contain an eternity, and with the burgeoning pace of ever more accurate clocks, the second is indeed opening up into a new universe of time. After Harrison's No. 4 Chronometer set a precedent for accuracy, it was inevitable that an even more accurate clock would be built. It happened in 1889. Siegmund Riefler of Germany constructed a clock that worked inside a partial vacuum to reduce the influence of air pressure on the moving parts. His device had an accuracy within a tenth of a second a day and could easily measure milliseconds, or thousandths of a second. It was at this point that clocks became capable of measuring actions that are beyond our ability to see . . . a housefly flapping its wings once every three milliseconds. But even Riefler's pre-eminence was short-lived.

In the 1920s, William H. Shortt, an English railroad engineer, built the first electromechanical clock. It was based on two clocks: a "master" and a "slave." The slave clock sent an electromagnetic impulse every thirty seconds to the pendulum master clock, which then, in turn, regulated the slave clock. This device was accurate to within one second a year, precise enough to measure microseconds, or millionths of a second. In a microsecond a sound wave will have moved only one-third of a millimetre.

Shortt's timekeeper was usurped only eight years later, when Warren A. Marrison, an engineer at Bell Laboratories in the United States, designed the first quartz-crystal clock, using the vibrational frequency of an electrically charged quartz crystal. By the mid-1940s, quartz clocks had achieved a degree of accuracy within one second every thirty years. The world of the very small—the crystal lattice of silicon molecules that make up quartz—had become the new pendulum.

The pace of precision timekeeping continued to accelerate. In 1948 Harold Lyons created the first atomic clock, using the natural resonant frequency of an atom. By the mid-1950s this atomic clock had evolved into the cesium-beam atomic clock, which is still in use today to broadcast Co-ordinated Universal Time and which has an accuracy of about one nanosecond a day. A nanosecond is a billionth of second, the time it takes light to travel thirty centimetres in a vacuum. Computers take between two to four nanoseconds to process a single calculation. The children's odyssey in C. S. Lewis's *The Lion, the Witch and the Wardrobe*, where an imagined lifetime of adventure is crammed into a couple of seconds, must have been scaled to nanoseconds, each second in that world equalling a nanosecond of ours.

This kind of accuracy has allowed scientists to measure the duration of a second, long defined (somewhat tautologically) as the "sixtieth part of the sixtieth part of the twenty-fourth part of a day." According to the cesium-beam atomic clock, a second is defined as the duration of 9,192,631,770 periods of the radiation corresponding to the transition between the two hyperfine levels of the ground state of the cesium-133 atom at zero degrees kelvin. It's not an elegant definition, but it's absolute.

◂　◂　◂

Clocks have become so accurate now that a curious thing has happened: they have outstripped the master clock—the earth's revolution—that clockmakers have always used to calibrate their most precise chronometers. With the advent of the atomic clock, the yearly slowing of the earth's revolutions could be measured accurately—and it turned out to be three milliseconds a year. The earth was now an unreliable time-piece. But that wasn't all: the earth was also becoming an *irregular* time-piece. When the Boxing Day tsunami of 2004 struck, it changed the angular momentum of the planet's spin, speeding it up like a spinning figure skater pulling her arms closer to her body. As a consequence our days are now three millionths of a second shorter. But the divorce of abstract time from earthly time is far from complete, and there is an ongoing battle between astronomers and physicists about what our atomic timepieces should be based on. Astronomers argue for "natural time," where leap seconds are added every few years to accommodate the slowing earth, while physicists argue for "technological time," the final separation of time from its earthly orgins. The earth might yet be relegated to chronological history.

◂ ◂ ◂

And all the while, smaller and smaller durations of time, like the bays within bays of a shoreline, continue to be discovered. The femtosecond, one millionth of a billionth of a second, was measured soon after the nanosecond. From the perspective of the femtosecond we humans are unmoving statues that exist an eternity. There could be a whole civilization overlapped with our own for whom femtoseconds are like our seconds. The Femtonians could be living invisibly among us as if we were so many figurines. Should their science became advanced enough, a genius among them might announce that the statues are not utterly unchanging, but that they are, in fact, moving! Controversy would erupt. It would be well known that, although most of the stat-ues' eyes are open, some are half-closed, while a minority are com-pletely closed. Using comparison photographs gathered from over a century, the Femtonian scientist would show how the eyelids of a par-ticular statue with half-closed eyes have moved incrementally over the decades. "Preposterous!" would be the response from the dissenting scientists. "How could statues move? I suppose next you'll be telling us they're alive?"

But the Femtonians have already been usurped by a smaller, faster civilization. Briefer even than femtoseconds are attoseconds, clocking at a staggeringly tiny portion of time: a billionth of a billionth of a second. From the perspective of an attosecond, one of our seconds lasts three million years, the same amount of time it took humans to evolve. Yet still smaller units of time are being sought after. David Blair, an Australian physicist, has built the most accurate clock yet in order to try and measure gravitational waves. Even though they knit our galaxy together, gravitational waves are ineffable, with extraordinarily weak emissions. They have never been detected. Blair hopes his new clock will be fast enough to catch them. His timepiece is not as stable as an atomic clock over long periods, but in the short term it is accurate to one part in a hundred trillion over three hundred seconds. At its heart is a sapphire crystal that is kept at −273° Celsius in a bath of liquid helium, capable of measuring a trillion-trillionth of a second.

At this scale of duration the only events that move fast enough to be measured are sub-atomic events: the lifetime of quarks and the breaking of atomic bonds. It is a jumpy, quivering world of electrons and particles. And that's where everything converges. If our coastline surveyors insisted on measuring the entire edge of their shoreline—attending to smaller and smaller inlets and points until they were accounting for edges of pebbles, then grains of sand, then molecules and finally the edges of atoms—they would arrive at the same place, the same time frame as a cesium clock. You have to have a very fast ruler to measure subatomic shorelines; they keep changing. There comes a point, at the infinitesimal scale of things, where not only time and mass converge but also gravity and light. In that tiny, furiously quick world, light moves like molasses and mass disappears into energy. Perhaps, as Blair hopes, the secret of gravity might be lurking there as well.

▴ ▴ ▴

But if clocks get more accurate, particularly if they become accurate to within a millisecond in three million years, then, due to relativistic effects, simply walking around with one will slow it down measurably. Also, elevation will change the pace, since time runs slower at the surface of the planet than higher up. This effect is already measurable. Due to relativity, clocks at the top of Mount Everest run faster than those at sea level, pulling ahead by about thirty microseconds a year. Time too, when reduced to its smallest parts, becomes slippery and indeterminate. It may well be that there is a limit beyond which the smallest portions of time cannot be measured.

And Yet . . .

"Now," from the perspective of an attosecond, is a very fleeting thing, impossible to seize. It makes our "now" seem to stretch for an eternity, at least relatively, even if, from our perspective, the present moment is as mercurial as any small division of time. Because it is all we have, this small moment is also the most precious, an oasis in the sands of time. Yet "now" has another scale, in the opposite direction from the abyss of milliseconds and nanoseconds. There is a bigger "now."

In terms of our consensual "now," the one we all agree on, we consciously occupy a slice, perhaps a quarter of a second, and that is our time frame. Most living things on the earth exist in the same "now" as we do. You could argue that starfish and plants exist in a "now" with a longer wavelength than ours; their purposeful movements can only be seen with time-lapse photography. Conversely, some insects and pygmy marmosets seem to exist in a faster, narrower "now." Computers, though not yet conscious or living beings, operate in an even briefer "now," just nanoseconds long. But these are the fine-grained "nows," like the fast end of my Olympic time clock. In the other direction, "now" is coarse.

When politicians or historians say "now," they often mean the current period, the "way certain things are" presently. That "now" is not as brief as the personal and universal "now," the vanishing trace that skims from past to future like a cursor carrying our awareness along with it. The cultural "now" can be much larger, a decade or longer, yet it is still correct to call it now. In that sense "now" can encompass centuries, even millennia.

In geological terms, "now" is very precisely located. It is nested within an increasingly bigger series of well-defined time periods. "Now" in geological terms is defined as the Holocene epoch, which began about eleven thousand years ago, while humans were still in the hunter-gatherer stage. The Holocene epoch is itself part of the Quaternary period, which started two million years ago. And the Quaternary period is only a small part of a much larger portion of time, the Cenozoic era, also called the age of mammals. It began roughly sixty-five million years ago, immediately after the Mesozoic era, the age of dinosaurs. So you could argue that in that sense "now" is sixty-five million years long.

From the perspective of that long, resounding "now," my neighbourhood transforms into an unfamiliar tableau, an interlude of stillness, a single frame in a time-lapse film that has been running since the beginning of the planet. The maples and oaks and hickories, whose crowns are solid with leaves, become opportunistic, temporary species inhabiting a brief niche in a tumultuous ecology of plants and creatures that appear, flourish and then die away. But the buildings amidst the trees take on an even stranger appearance. These comfortable brick houses I can see from my study window transform into something almost peculiar—the geometric dwellings of a particularly successful species of primate that, in the blink of an eye, has covered the planet.

Chapter Four

ZENO'S HORSE: MANIPULATING TIME

I might have slept through a lesser storm, but last night Zeus was out for blood. A window-rattling bang woke me with my heart skidding. As soon as I opened my eyes, the bedroom was lit up by a lightning flash, then another, then a peal of thunder that sounded like house-sized boulders being dropped on a steel floor. Sleep was out of the question. I got up and went to the window. Outside was pandemonium. Lightning flashed every few seconds, each stroke followed instantly by thunder. The storm was right on top of me. No steamboats.

The branches of the tree in front of my house were flailing in terrific gusts, and the almost continuous flickering of the purple-white lightning—like a strobe light—captured the movement of the leaves and branches in stop-motion. I saw the wet green of the new maple leaves as they twisted and fluttered in the wind. Above the tree, lightning bolts laced the sky like instant maps of dazzling rivers.

It was a terrific spectacle, and I watched until the gaps between the lightning and the thunder stretched longer and longer and the flashes began to fade in the distance. Finally the storm abated, on its way to the countryside to startle sleeping cattle and to drench fields. I went back to bed thankful I wasn't camping.

This morning I got up to a quiet, sunny day, the second Friday of May. Except for wet soil and some downed branches on the back lawn, you'd never guess at the violence of the night before. But the flowers on the rhododendron in my back garden had begun to unclench. They had been reluctant all week amid the fading glories of the daffodils and tulips, holding their spade-shaped buds closed like pointed temple domes. By noon I could see small, crimson puffs where the petals of individual flowers were emerging from their clusters. I sat down on the lawn beside the rhododendron and improvised a special state of mind. I slowed myself down, became calm. I tried to remember what few shreds of meditation I had learned years ago to slow my metabolism. It was so quiet that I could hear the buzz of insects orbiting nearby flowers.

I don't know if I convinced myself that I could see the rhododendron flowers actually blooming, yet I'm sure I watched them open a little in the half-hour I sat looking at them, although knowledge sometimes corrupts experience. Maybe I superimposed memories of flowers blossoming in a time-lapse film I'd seen once. Or did I indeed slow my own time scale to a speed that accelerated the rhododendron's opening? It didn't matter in the end. The flowers were a cellular extravaganza; they inflated like miniature lavender thunderheads as myriads of cells divided and divided again inside them. Each petal was granular, with water-plump, semi-transparent cells. The flowers were soft, velvety to the touch. Within them a powerful surge of liquids and sugars pumped them larger and larger. Yet it *was* slow.

I got up and went back into the house. The interior was cool compared to the backyard, and the oak staircase leading to the second floor was fragrant in the humidity and slightly moist to the touch. I worked for a few hours and later that afternoon went out to look at the rhododendron. Six flower clusters had now fully opened. Their purple petals were glossy and perfect in the hot sun, and the tips of their stamens, deep within the cool, amethyst chambers of their cups, were already dusted with pollen. Everything else was blossoming as well: the lilies, the hostas, even my neighbour's mock orange. But the maples were way ahead. They had lost their flowers, and clusters of winged seeds hung from the branches amidst the leaves. Too soon, it seemed. Sooner every year. A flower in the tree, a seed in the flower, a tree in the seed.

THE STANFORD PEGASUS

One sunny June morning in 1878, at a racetrack in Palo Alto, California, the world changed. Eadweard Muybridge stopped time. The cameras he used to freeze a galloping horse in mid-stride had been invented only thirty-nine years earlier by Louis Jacques Mandé Daguerre, and by today's standards the photographic technology of the Victorian era was still very primitive. But Muybridge was a visionary and an inventor. He tweaked an extraordinary performance out of his modified daguerreotype cameras and that morning they revealed a new realm of time. Within days newspapers around the world were printing hand-drawn copies of his equine photographs (newspapers could not yet reproduce photographs), and Muybridge became famous.

An inventor as well as a grand eccentric in the Victorian tradition, Muybridge had immigrated to America from England at an early age, settling in San Francisco. As a young man he became fascinated by the new medium of photography and quickly developed a reputation as a landscape photographer. Over the previous two decades photography had revolutionized portraiture and landscape art. People unable to afford paintings of themselves or their children or of picturesque landscapes could now hire photographers.

There was something magic about photographs, particularly of people. These were not painted interpretations, but direct images. Time was arrested at the point at which the photograph was taken, allowing people to revisit the past directly, through these little windows into history. It was the beginning of a kind of virtual time travel that we now take for granted. We hardly ever marvel at the fact that when you look into the lens of a camera that's about to take your picture, you're looking into the future, while posterity looks back at you out of its glass eye.

I've always been fascinated by a daguerreotype of my grandmother taken when she was a young woman in Europe. She is in half profile, her hair up in a languorous coiffure, a few studied strands trailing over her ears. She is wearing a tailored dress with a high, elegant collar adorned with a silver pin. Her shoulders are draped in a fur wrap, and a magnificent black ostrich-feather hat surmounts everything. She is striking. And she is young, perhaps only eighteen. There is something immediately accessible about this photograph; it seems much more recent than its hundred and ten years. You can see by a faint stiffness to her pose that the photographer had told her to remain still. The exposure must have taken a few seconds.

It was this limitation of still photography that irked Muybridge. He wanted to go further into the instantaneous, to photograph the moving world. He began to experiment with new lenses and shutters to increase the speed of his camera, and by 1870 his diligence had paid off. His pioneering photographs of moving people and animals astonished audiences at exhibitions, and his work gained him a national reputation. Leland Stanford, a retired railway engineer and horse breeder, invited him to his ranch in Sacramento, where, in 1873, he began to fund Muybridge's research into motion photography.

Muybridge used Stanford's horses as his subjects, photographing them as they walked, trotted and galloped. In order to photograph the thoroughbreds, he had to improve his shutter speed even further. Normally, the daguerreotype cameras of his day had an exposure time of several seconds; sitting for a portrait, as my grandmother had done, meant that you had to remain absolutely still for the duration of the exposure. This would not do for a galloping horse. Muybridge developed faster shutter speeds and film until, by 1877, he had achieved a shutter speed of 1/2,000 of a second, at the limit of what the most accurate clocks of his day could measure. He could now photograph a world previously invisible to the human eye: the realm of the super-fast.

Stanford had an ulterior motive for hiring Muybridge. In the nineteenth century there was an ongoing argument as to whether or not a galloping horse ever lifted all four hooves off the ground. One side, the pragmatists, claimed that a running horse needed to have at least one hoof on the ground: otherwise it would stumble. The other side, the romantics, said that a horse became airborne in mid-stride, and they called their version of equine locomotion "unsupported transit." It was a difficult point to settle. Neither group could claim precedence because no one could actually see what was going on beneath a galloping horse. Anything that takes place in less than a tenth of second is beyond our ability to discern clearly.

On the morning of June 14, 1878, racing enthusiasts and newspapermen lined the track at Leland Stanford's Palo Alto Stock Farm. On one side of the track stood a whitewashed shed with a long, horizontal window that opened at waist level. Poking through the window, like cannons through portholes, were a dozen cameras, each fitted with two lenses. Across from them Muybridge had set up a white canvas backdrop marked with vertical lines at two-foot intervals. The track had been laid with electric trip wires to trigger each of the cameras' shutters in succession as the horse ran by.

When everything was ready the horse and rider set off on their journey into time and history. The cameras worked without a hitch. Muybridge quickly developed the photos and the results were stunning:

perfect images of horse and rider caught in frames of time less than 1/2,000 of second long. And when the horse was in mid-stride, all four hooves were off the ground. The "unsupported transit" believers won the day. Human perception, assisted by technology, had moved beyond its natural limits. Time within time began to open up.

As reproductions of these photographs began to circulate around the world, visual artists were especially intrigued. French poet and art critic Paul Valéry wrote that Muybridge's pictures "laid bare all the mistakes that sculptors and painters had made in their renderings of the various postures of the horse." This was true. The "hobby horse" pose used by painters to depict galloping horses before Muybridge—both front and hind legs extended—was proven incorrect. Some artists, like Edgar Degas, welcomed this realism. Others were outraged. The sculptor Auguste Rodin declared, "It is the artist who is truthful and it is photography which lies, for in reality, time does not stop." He had a point: time doesn't stop. But he was also being disingenuous. A high-speed photograph takes a slice out of time, and that slice has certainly stopped.

In the end, the Palo Alto spectacle was a photo op. Muybridge and Stanford likely knew the outcome of their drama. But the flies that Stanford's horses swatted off their shanks with their tails while they were waiting at the starting gate had yet to be captured on film. The hummingbird's wings had yet to be stilled. It was only a matter of time before they too would be caught in photographic emulsion, like insects in amber.

ELECTRIC TIME

Today I phoned a naturalist, a nocturnal animal-call expert who lives in Ithaca, New York. I was lucky to get him in. I wanted him to identify the owl that I'd seen in March, because on other nights I had also heard its call. Yesterday I'd been on the Web and downloaded a call from an owl site, but it wasn't right. I downloaded some other likely calls, but couldn't get them to play on my computer. Frustrated, I turned to Lang Elliott. I told him my problem and crudely imitated the trill that I'd heard earlier in the spring. "Give me a second," he said. He scanned his library of recorded owl calls and played for me what he thought was the best candidate. It was exactly the call I'd heard. As always (I'd phoned him before about other calls), he was right on the money. "Eastern screech-owl," he said. "Not uncommon in cities."

There's something about the phone—the immediacy and instant intimacy—that I still prefer over the Internet. With specialists I can always get more quickly to the information I need. Telephone technology was only two years old when Muybridge photographed Stanford's Pegasus, yet a telephone set had already been installed in the White House. President Rutherford B. Hayes knew a winner when he saw one.

◢ ◢ ◢

The telephone was the child of the telegraph, which had been proliferating across the country since the first message was sent by Samuel Morse in 1844, more than three decades earlier. It's hard to say which was more revolutionary, the telephone or the telegraph, but the effect of instant communication across a great distance was revolutionary. The time once occupied by space had been cancelled at the speed of light.

After Morse's inaugural message, the subsequent acceptance and growth of the telegraph was extraordinary. It completely outpaced the adoption of any previous technology. By 1851 the first transatlantic cable had been laid, and by 1861 North America was criss-crossed from coast to coast with telegraph wire. Speed became everything. The telegraph meant that news from distant events took minutes instead of days to reach far-flung places, and as telegraph lines began to stretch into Asia and the other continents, the concept of a global "now" inserted itself into the average citizen's consciousness, at least in Western nations. Great solitudes of time and remoteness were drawn into the electric web. This global "now" was further reinforced when U.S. railroads initiated central time signals. In 1851 the first time-beats were sent across the railway network from the Harvard College Observatory in Cambridge, thereby synchronizing all railway clocks across the four newly instated time zones of the United States to within a second.

It is worth noting here that the institution of time zones was also the initiation of an invidious process, one that has been accelerated by atomic clocks in the present—namely, the divorce of time from the earth. The abstraction of time zones meant that "noon" was no longer dependent on the position of the sun. The angle of the sun is different at one edge of a time zone than the other, even though the clocks in both places register noon. As clocks became more precise, the separation of abstract time from earthly time grew larger, until, as we have seen, the earth itself became outmoded as an accurate timepiece. But these anomalies hardly gave pause during the breathless growth of new technologies in the nineteenth century.

Newspapers also proliferated and expanded as the appetite for world events grew. Somewhere in that decade after the invention of the telegraph, a reporter filed the first electronic report from the field. By 1848 several large American dailies had realized the immense potential of the telegraph as a news-gathering (and news-distributing) medium. They formed a collective organization for sharing news by linked telegraphs, which eventually became known as the Associated Press. But the telegraph was just the beginning of time-altering media.

◂ ◂ ◂

The pace of invention and change in the mid-nineteenth century was astounding: photography in 1839, the telegraph in 1844, the phonograph and telephone in 1877. Even Victorian clergymen, such as the English author Charles Kingsley, were caught up in the technological hubris. In 1848 he wrote, "Give me the political economist, the sanitary reformer, the engineer; and take your saints and virgins, relics and miracles. The spinning-jenny and the railroad, Cunard's liners and the electric telegraph, are to me ... signs that we are, on some points at least, in harmony with the universe."

More harmony was on the way. In 1878 the first telephone exchange came into operation, and Alexander Graham Bell introduced telephones to England. Six years later reliable long-distance connections existed between Boston, Massachusetts, and New York City, though it wasn't until the next century that a successful transatlantic phone cable was laid. Telephone networks existed in most industrialized nations by 1900. Benjamin Franklin may have coined the phrase "Time is money," but Alexander Graham Bell was the first to turn time into coin, long-distance charges being the most direct translation of time into money ever.

The telephone not only linked two people, it linked separate geographical locations. The telephone, as Marshall McLuhan once quipped, allows you to be in two places at once. It seems a facile observation but it's quite true. If the person at the other end of the line is beside an ocean and they hold their phone to a window, you'll hear the waves. It's not just a conversation: separate ambiences also overlap. The sounds around you at your end of the line blend with the background sounds at the other end. Telephones collapse geographical space into personal space.

But something also happens to time. When people are asked to estimate the amount of time they spent on a phone call, they consistently come up short. Could it be that time and space are so intimately linked that it also takes twice as much perceived time to be in two places at once? It's hard to say. My phone call to Lang Elliott was short, perhaps a few minutes, though I'll see the real duration when I get the bill. I won't argue it. My phone company has been in business for a hundred and thirty years.

THE TIME MIRROR: BIRTH OF THE CINEMA

The closing decades of the nineteenth century heralded the arrival of the most extraordinary manipulation of time ever, though it had been gestating in middle-class parlours for decades before. The Victorian obsession with moving images began with the introduction of the phenakistoscope in 1832. The phenakistoscope was a slotted disc with a series of images, usually dancing or juggling figures, arranged around its outer margin. When the disc was spun in front of a mirror, you could look through the whirling slots and see the reflected figures moving. The Victorians were hooked. The phenakistoscope was succeeded by a series of tongue-twisting gizmos: the zoetrope in 1867; Reynaud's praxinoscope in 1877; and, finally, Eadweard Muybridge's own contribution, the zoopraxiscope in 1879, which had the added feature of being able to project images onto a screen from photographs printed on a glass disc.

All of these motion picture forerunners, in common with today's cinema, relied on the lower limit of our speed of perception. The eye blended individual "frames" when the revolving discs reached a certain threshold velocity. The key achievement was the illusion of smooth, continuous movement. Like Zeno's Arrow, each image was still in and of itself, but when each successive image was combined in a series, movement emerged miraculously. It was the opposite of Muybridge's strategy: instead of capturing movement too fast to be seen, the illusion of movement was achieved by tricking the eye. And when photography was blended with this technology, something entirely new was created—a kind of time mirror that could play back what it had reflected. The arrow flew.

In the beginning these "moving picture" experiences were very personal. Only one or two people could look into the zoetrope or the first praxinoscopes. Moving pictures did not become a group experience until the early 1890s, when Charles-Émile Reynaud devised a way to project his praxinoscope onto a screen.

Then Thomas Edison got involved. Fresh from inventing another time-based medium, the phonograph, he decided to tackle motion pictures. Together with his assistant William Dickson, he designed and built the kinetoscope in 1892. In the beginning it was a coin-operated device for penny arcades, but he later adopted a projector that used an optical lantern to project the action onto a screen. Dickson also standardized the width of movie film at thirty-five millimetres and invented a precise, motor-driven shutter and sprocket system to feed the unexposed film through the camera at a constant rate. Their equipment permitted the rapid growth of the motion picture industry—it was a gold mine.

Edison's first penny-arcade style Kinetoscope Parlor, the forerunner of the movie theatre, opened in New York City in 1894. The "movies" were more like film clips, and they had titles such as *Trapeze*, *Wrestling*, *Barber Shop*, *Blacksmiths* and *Cock Fight*. But people loved them. Soon, other kinetoscope parlours opened in Atlantic City, San Francisco and Chicago. Meanwhile, in France, the Lumière brothers, Louis and Auguste, built an all-in-one movie camera and projector. It was handheld and portable and could be hand-cranked. The Lumières called their invention the *cinématographe*, and they patented it in 1895. The film speed they settled on—sixteen frames per second—became the industry norm until the advent of sound film in the late 1920s, when twenty-four frames per second prevailed. They showed their first films in Paris in 1895. Much more dramatic than the scenes of daily life found in the Edison films, the Lumières' scenes of a train entering a station or a horse-drawn carriage galloping towards the camera had audiences gasping.

In 1897 the first movie theatre, replete with projector and screen, opened in Paris. Five years later the Electric Theatre opened in Los Angeles, and Georges Méliès and the Lumière brothers began making films in earnest, creating hundreds of them by the turn of the century. Méliès even screened the first popular science-fiction film, *Le voyage dans la lune (A Trip to the Moon)*, in 1902. It premiered several film techniques: a narrative storyline, a plot, trick photography, dissolves, superimpositions, stop-motion and slow motion. In 1903 Edwin S. Porter's ten-minute opus western, *The Great Train Robbery*, heralded the beginning of many film techniques still in use today. Porter developed film editing, and as a result *The Great Train Robbery* was one of the earliest films to be shot out of chronological sequence. It also featured cross-cutting between simultaneous scenes, one scene with rear projection and two panning shots. The wholesale manipulation of narrative time—of condensing hours and days into minutes—had commenced.

THE BEGINNING OF MODERN TIMES

Were you alive in 1902, a typical Saturday afternoon might find you paying your phone bill or going through your stereograph collection. Stereographs were three-dimensional photographs, almost like holograms, that were viewed through a hand-held device called a stereoscope. But they were better than photographs, because they were like being there. Looking into the stereoscope, you left your body behind and went on a trip through time and space. You could visit exotic places and people, and you could witness, first-hand, great news stories of the recent past—train wrecks and battlefields.

A little later you might go out to a movie theatre and see time sped up with stop-motion photography. Back at home you could put on a record and listen to popular music, a time-based art performance captured like a photograph. You might make a long-distance phone call to a friend in another city. By 1902 time was already highly mutable. Instantaneous where it had once been delayed (instead of waiting days for a letter, you could telegraph or telephone immediately), and mixed where it had once been continuous (in films, bits and pieces from the past as well from imagined futures combined themselves with the present). Time became putty in the hands of the media.

TIME-LAPSE PHOTOGRAPHY

The flicker of film or of malfunctioning fluorescent lights provides a sort of ambient time-lapse effect close to, but not as intense as, the effect of a stroboscopic light in a dark room. There is nothing quite like the feeling of dancing under a strobe light—it's like visiting another world. Your disassociated movements, time-sampled by the strobe, take on a fluid, trailing grace. Time-lapse photography is similar, though the spaces between each sample, or frame, are longer and the duration has been removed. It is really time compression. Successive frames of a movie are captured at a rate slower than they are projected. When replayed at normal speed, time is accelerated. Incremental processes that are normally too slow to be seen, like plant growth or stars wheeling through the night sky, are revealed by this technique.

Time-lapse photography appeared for the first time in 1897, in a feature film by Georges Méliès called *Carrefour de l'opéra*. It was an astonishing novelty, though cinematographers continued to elaborate its potential. The technique reached a high point sixty years later with John Ott's 1956 documentary *The Secrets of Life*. Ott's sequences of blossoms opening in full colour had all the beauty and dynamism of fireworks. I saw the film as a child, and it no doubt inspired me the day I watched my rhododendron flowers opening.

I wonder if H. G. Wells wasn't inspired likewise—not by Ott of course, but by Méliès. For Wells, *The Time Machine*, published close to the release of *Carrefour de l'opéra*, contains a visionary passage that describes his protagonist's journey into the future. The resemblance to time-lapse films is unmistakable:

> As I put on pace, night followed day like the flapping of a black wing. The dim suggestion of the laboratory seemed presently to fall away from me, and I saw the sun hopping swiftly across the sky, leaping it every minute, and every minute marking a day. I supposed the laboratory had been destroyed and I had come into the open air. I had a dim impression of scaffolding, but I was already going too fast to be conscious of any moving things. The slowest snail that ever crawled dashed by too fast for me. The twinkling succession of darkness and light was excessively painful to the eye. Then, in the intermittent darknesses, I saw the moon spinning swiftly through her quarters from new to full, and had a faint glimpse of the circling stars. Presently, as I went on, still gaining velocity, the palpitation of night and day merged into one continuous greyness; the sky took on a wonderful deepness of blue, a splendid luminous

colour like that of early twilight; the jerking sun became a streak of fire, a brilliant arch, in space; the moon a fainter fluctuating band; and I could see nothing of the stars, save now and then a brighter circle flickering in the blue.

Time-lapse photography, at least in the twentieth century, became the purview of documentaries showing the building of bridges, spiders constructing webs, fruit rotting and, more recently, as exemplified in the 1983 film *Koyaanisqatsi*, clouds, traffic and cities. (Time-lapse films of clouds completely changed how I saw them. As a child I thought of clouds as single entities, as in Wordsworth's line from "The Daffodils": "I wandered lonely as a cloud." But time-lapse films showed me that clouds are more like puffs of steam forming continuously over one spot on the landscape.) Now time-lapse imagery is as commonplace as the fast-forward feature on home video players, through which, in a form of virtual time travel, scenes can be slowed down, speeded up, run backwards or played in slow motion.

SLOW MOTION

Slow motion had to wait for cameras that could capture more than sixteen frames a second, the limit of the first kinetoscope cameras designed by Edison. It is a testament to how fast movie-making evolved that by 1894 the French cinematographer Étienne-Jules Marey constructed a camera that could record seven hundred frames per second, though his technique did not reach mainstream cinema until much later. In 1904 the German August Musger filed the first patent for a slow-motion film camera, but it lapsed, and the Ernemann Company of Dresden introduced an almost identical slow-motion technique in 1914. Slow motion soon became a standard part of filmmaking, and several directors used it effectively, particularly after playback speed jumped from sixteen to twenty-four frames a second. Akira Kurosawa was one of the earliest directors to use slow motion, showcasing it in his 1954 movie *The Seven Samurai*. Later, Sam Peckinpah used it to heighten the realism of violence in his films. More recently, ultra-slow motion and a technique now known as "bullet motion" were used extensively in *The Matrix*.

With the advent of computer-assisted cinematography, it became possible to play various aspects of a scene at actual speed while other aspects played in slow motion or were even stopped. So an actor could walk through frozen explosions as if they were museum dioramas. Currently, in film and video, time can be divided, run backwards, forwards, divided and run forwards and backwards simultaneously, slowed down and speeded up in an infinite number of combinations. We get to play God with time, assembling a new timescape out of digital pulses and celluloid.

But it is only slow motion that lets us experience time from the perspective of the ultra-fast, like our Femtonian friends. There is a graceful, floating quality to slow motion that smoothes out the jumpiness of real time. A slow-motion film of a drop of water falling into a pond becomes a symphony of liquid geometry. The wobbling, elliptical drop disappears into the water amid a perfectly circular wave that rises like a glass crown. But then, astonishingly, as the crown subsides, the drop rises up again from the centre on a stalk of liquid. As it falls back and is replaced by still another rebounding drop, the crown flattens into a ripple. This is something no one could have imagined, or seen, before.

In slow motion the instinctual movements of a cat become pure choreography. Dropped with its back to the ground, a cat executes a mid-air ballet as it deftly twists itself upright just before a perfect four-point landing on the grass. If we could enter the world of slow motion, we would become the quick-moving, jerky figures we see in time-lapse photography. But there are occasions when we *do* enter the world of slow motion in real life, when, for instance, we are accelerated by a traumatic event. Several years ago my daughter and I were in a triple streetcar accident in Toronto, and I experienced first-hand the power of adrenaline to slow time.

◂ ◂ ◂

It was a late spring afternoon, almost twilight. We were on a north-bound streetcar passing through the middle of an intersection when a westbound streetcar blindsided us. It was quite an impact. At first I didn't know what had happened. My daughter and I were sitting at the back, and there was an incredible percussion as the whole street-car lurched to one side. It was such a large noise that it was somehow strangely muted, more like a shape than a sound. When I look back now, I think my hearing must have been affected by my adrenaline cutting in, because that's when time really slowed down. What happened next took place in lucid slow motion.

The impact of the westbound streetcar knocked us off the rails and sent our streetcar sliding sideways up the street. Trailing glass, sparks and metal, we skidded towards an oncoming southbound streetcar that was already too close to stop. My window faced the driver of the approaching streetcar. His eyes met mine, and an acknowledgement of some sort passed between us. Then he broke off his gaze. I could see the tendons in his arms as he furiously, but agonizingly slowly, pumped some kind of hand-brake lever. I could also see the lights of the advertisements in his streetcar and the stoic, clenched looks on the passengers' faces.

Then he hit us. It was a tremendous collision, and the entire view swung away. Everyone in our streetcar who hadn't already been knocked out of their seats went flying across the aisles. I remember seeing the safety glass erupt into the interior like floating mist, and there was a kind of smell, not of burning, but a sharp, high smell, almost chemical. All of this took place in deafening silence. Then, like a film resuming normal speed, everything started happening in real time, and I was surrounded by noise. People moaning, crying, the tinkle of glass still crumbling out of the windows and the hiss of air escaping from a broken pneumatic brake.

Fortunately my daughter and I were unhurt, though a day or so afterwards I noticed two bruises on my hips, one on each side. My adrenaline must have completely anesthetized me. I've read reports of others who've had similar experiences of slow-motion time during accidents or during competitive sporting games, so it seems we are able to experience accelerated time for brief periods. But we cannot experience anything like what high-speed film can capture now—bullets slowly plunging through apples, hovering hummingbirds flapping their wings at the speed of a crow.

◂ ◂ ◂

Photography opened up a frontier of perception that has entertained, astonished and informed us like nothing else. With new eyes we look into a world of time that was once shut away from us. If I were to set up a time-lapse camera in my backyard, my garden would be almost unrecognizable. The rising stems of the peonies would writhe and extend like leafy fingers reaching blindly out of the soil. My tulips would flip open each morning and snap shut at night. The tendrils of the clematis would grope like octopus tentacles as they climbed the trellis beside the patio. There would be purpose here, for at this speed the difference between plant and animal disappears.

MEDIA TIME NOW

> The modern world abridges all historical times as readily
> as it reduces space. Every*where* and every *age* have become
> *here* and *now*. History has been abolished by our new
> media.
> —*Marshall McLuhan*, Understanding Media

Here, at the beginning of a new millennium, time is just another medium, one of many vying for our attention. Clock signals are electronically relayed around the world, they course through our computers, televisions, radios and telephones. The globe is connected in a single, precise instant that ticks inexorably onwards wherever we are.

We know this, and we know our biological clock ticks onwards too, yet we sometimes act as if we don't really believe it, and we seem to believe it less and less every decade. Why? Because we are the inheritors of a century of time manipulation in films, television, pop music (with its sampled repetitions) and telecommunications. We call people in different time zones, so the sun can be shining brightly through our windows while we speak to someone watching the moon rise through theirs. Time has become at once both complex and infinitely malleable.

Live international television broadcasts and jets have shrunk the world, as the adage has it. Distance isn't what it used to be. But they have also shrunk time, at least time in the older, grander sense. Our instantaneous, multi-tasking workplaces allow us to fit more work into shorter periods of time, and as we become increasingly wireless our private realm shrinks accordingly; everyone is connected to everyone else all the time. This comes with a price, for our bodies have their own sense of time, which arose out of the cycles of the natural world, from the alternation of night and day. Personal retreat distance and privacy are becoming scarce, and there is hardly any time to reflect, to meditate, to drift—natural states of mind that allow us the freedom to disengage from the world. Disengagement has become a luxury. Taking your time has become a recreational indulgence.

On television the flow of time is constantly interrupted by commercials that are paragons of time condensation. How do you sell your product in thirty seconds? Film techniques of editing and narrative compression are honed to their essence here. Recently it seems that the flow of time itself is the theme of some television ads. The ability to digitize films and separate the various action components of a scene and then play them at different speeds is now a cliché in automobile commercials. Cars cruise at normal speed under time-lapse clouds, or winter turns to spring in the wake of a sleek sedan. How advertisers capture our viewing time for their own ends has turned into the central struggle of our temporal economy, and as communications media fuse with entertainment media, the tussle feels increasingly intimate, even invasive.

THE GREAT ATTRACTOR

> The future ain't what it used to be.
> —*Yogi Berra*

We are all passengers of "now"; this is our common bond. If we were suddenly transported to another century, we would be temporally and culturally marooned, wandering like orphans through an alien sensibility. If we came upon other time travellers from our own time, we would greet them like brothers or sisters, no matter what country they were from, because the bond of "now" is probably even stronger than nationality. But our "now" is a Hollywood concoction, the result of a century of time manipulation by various media, and it stretches from the Jurassic era to the distant future.

Time-based art forms, particularly television and cinema, have brought representations of all periods—past, present and future—into our timeless present. Here, in McLuhan's "end of history," all fashions, all cultures, all stories exist at once. This puts us in a special situation, a paradoxical one, where the present, with its idiomatic sayings, dress codes and assumptions, is advantaged over not just the past but the future as well. The evolution of fashion, if such a thing could be said to exist, is now stymied by a future that we've already visited. There is nowhere to go.

The future, at least as it looks in science fiction films, is either inhabited by the kind of people who attend *Star Trek* conventions or a high-tech showroom where villainous scientists battle oppressed heroes in a dysfunctional society. Everyone seems to be dressed in vaguely utilitarian designer clothes, like discards from Pierre Cardin's abstract-modernist line of the 1960s. It is certainly no place for the urbane sophisticates of today's popular culture. For them, the future is only slightly more repellent than the earnestness of the recent past. But within that recent past, the last thirty years or so, there is something that pop culture keeps circling back to, as if there were a kind of cultural black hole, a grand attractor that has warped time around it. The present can't seem to get beyond it, can't reach escape velocity.

The only way today's fashionistas are able to ward off the painful earnestness of the past and yet still rummage through it for "new" looks is with special talismans, the irony of "retro" accessories. This irony lets them sample the past without stigma while appropriating its enduring charisma. Perhaps an anxiety lurks behind our timeless present, a sort of claustrophobia. It may be unconscious, but it is irrevocably there, its hum underscoring our restless nostalgia. We are trapped somehow. And the gravitational time-centre of our nostalgia seems to be located somewhere in the late sixties, even for those born decades later. Like a massive stellar object, its tremendous "retro" gravity sucks the future back into it, halting the forward progression of cultural time. But if the great attractor is a lost paradise that we can watch, that we can mimic, we still cannot inhabit it, even if we dress the part.

What was it about that period that is so compelling now? Was it people's unquestioning faith in the future? Was it the technology? Certainly, the American manned space program, including six moon landings between 1969 and 1972, was a technological high-water mark that has dwarfed anything since. And then there were the regular super-sonic passenger flights of the Concorde, which, like the last remnant of a glorious age, outlasted the peak of Western culture by two decades. This period was also marked by unprecedented liberalism, from topless bathing suits to love-ins. The only living vestiges of our once-promised future—where lunar colonies and civilian space travel would have been commonplace—are the Internet, personal computers, digital toys, cell-phones and next year's car designs. And even car designers have suc-cumbed to the retro impulse with the resurrection of the Volkswagen Beetle, Mini Cooper and Ford Thunderbird.

Perhaps history hasn't really ended, as McLuhan pronounced, but it has certainly stalled. When nostalgia erupts so persistently into the present, then the forward movement of history, particularly one with-out a future to pull it forward, is arrested. As Herman Melville wrote, "The poor old Past, The Future's slave," and in the normal state of affairs the future does completely determine the past. All the past can do is freeze the gestures made by the future as it touches the present. But in the present cultural era, which began sometime in the late 1980s, when "retro" really burst forth in earnest with period-mixing films like Tim Burton's *Batman* (in which the technology and design mixed elements of the twenties, forties and eighties), both the past and the future seem to be slaves to the present. Meanwhile, the present is looking "elsewhen."

The late sixties were a technological high-water mark, but they stand in microcosm to the previous high points of human achievement: the Roman Empire, the Egyptian and Mayan civilizations. It's almost as if, as a species, we have a fear of success. But then, over time, civilizations rise and fall, like waves. So perhaps we will again rise to the engineering heights attained in the late sixties, will again have manned missions to the moon and supersonic passenger jets. But until then we at least have our digital media, and the chronosphere that they create.

The timeless "now" staged by celebrity culture is further underscored by the unnatural agelessness of its stars. Because of plastic surgery, they seem to occupy a null space in the flow of years. They are timeless beacons, Dorian Grays. George Hamilton (preserved with a perpetual tan like a Danish peat-bog mummy) once quipped that his peeling sunburn revealed a tan from 1955. When "ageless" stars finally flame out, the spectacle, as chronicled in tabloids, is mesmerizing. It is like watching a vampire impaled with a silver stake. They pass from youth to old age in the span of a few years.

◂ ◂ ◂

Of course, we've been exposed to nested time periods—at least historic ones—for thousands of years, when you consider the architecture of cities. Any large city has old and new buildings side-by-side—Art Deco beside Mies van der Rohe, Louis Sullivan beside Frank Gehry—and in older European cities these architectural periods can be hundreds of years apart, medieval churches beside Bauhaus office buildings. Rome, already known as the "eternal city," is one of the most extraordinary examples of different time periods existing cheek by jowl. It is a chronopolis, an archipelago of eras, so that a walk through Rome is a kind of random time travel, taking visitors and residents forwards and backwards willy-nilly, thousands of years at once. The Pantheon has stood intact, like an architectural living fossil, for millennia. It has presided over the rise and ruin of the Colosseum, outlasted empires and religions. Modern office towers soar beside it, and under the greatest palace of Rome, the Palazzo Venezia, lie Etruscan tombs.

Real Time and Time Lags

In a media world of unreal time—where daily talk shows and the evening news are pre-taped, where *Star Trek* rubs shoulders with documentary footage from the First World War—broadcasts that are genuinely live have an instant cachet. The Olympics, live sports programs, unfolding disasters, car chases, all draw huge audiences. But a few years ago, another, more complicated kind of live broadcast arose—"real time"—and two-way video conferencing was one of the first examples. Video conferencing purported to take place "in real time" because a computer processed the signals so quickly that there was no delay between sender and receiver, something that had not been possible earlier. The result was a two-way visual phone conversation. Nothing radical in that, or so it seemed. But the fact that a computer was working furiously to translate, send and then untranslate the digital signals subtended the whole process. It wasn't like video surveillance, which might also be said to take place in real time, but which merely reflects reality; there is no processing of the signal. Real time is synonymous with a kind of hyper-time, where electronic circuits race furiously just to stay in the present moment. It is as if the higher the price paid to be here and now, the more privileged the present moment.

The term "real time" was readily adopted and assigned to all sorts of things—for instance, the stock market crawlers that tick away at the bottom of your screen, or the "real-time four-wheel-drive" feature of some sport/utility vehicles (SUVs), which automatically switches from two- to four-wheel drive when you go off-road. Real time means that we are moving so fast we have caught up to the present—which waits for no one, save the fastest.

So "real time" is a commodity, something you can buy if you have enough money, unlike those who are marooned in what must be "unreal time," where computers aren't fast enough and cars don't have automatic asymmetrical 4WD. (In one sense, "real time" is reminiscent of "quality time," those hours that busy people snatch between appointments and jobs to be with their children.) On the other hand, television's version of "real time" is trickier, particularly in live broadcasts. Sometimes people do or say things that networks would prefer they didn't, and so broadcasts have a built-in time delay of several seconds that allows producers to hit a "dump" button and delete the offending sequence. We don't notice a built-in time lag the way we notice the delay of an audio feed on a live television report from halfway around the world, where reporters blankly wait for the anchor's next question. Yet there are other built-in time lags—one military and the other biological—that are almost completely invisible.

In the command-and-control situation room of modern battleships, a wall-mounted screen shows real-time positions of enemy boats, planes and missiles. During the Falkland Islands war in 1982, H.M.S. *Sheffield's* radar defence shield was down temporarily while a satellite phone call was made back to Fleet Headquarters in England. When the radar screen came back online, it showed two enemy planes, thirty-three kilometres away—much too close for comfort, and, as it turned out, too late for response. Exocet guided missiles were already skimming towards H.M.S. *Sheffield*, just above the waves, at the speed of sound. There was not enough time to launch electronic counter-measures. All the officers could do was helplessly watch as the incoming blips tracked closer and closer.

But there was a further wrinkle. Because missiles and jets move quickly, most situation screens for both land and naval battle zones have built into them a computerized time delay of slightly more than 0.2 seconds. This delay counteracts the minimum human reaction time. The delay had been built into the command-and-control screen of *Sheffield*, which meant that—like a sinister video game—the officers saw the missile hit the target on the screen a moment before the ship itself exploded into flame.

Our 0.2-second reaction time is itself affected by a deeper neuro-logical phenomenon, one that some neurologists believe is proof of an immaterial soul. A few decades ago, a neurophysiologist by the name of Benjamin Libet discovered a perplexing paradox about the nervous system and the brain. During brain operations, when patients were conscious and parts of their cortex were exposed, Libet conducted experiments on how long it took for a pain impulse to reach the cortex, and then how long it took for the patient to report the pain. With the patient's consent he would prick the skin and measure when the incoming impulses hit the part of the brain that represented that area.

A pain impulse takes only 15/1,000 of a second to reach the cortex, but the brain takes half a second to translate that signal into conscious awareness. You can see the spikes on an oscillograph wired directly into the brain; it's hard science. Yet all patients reported the sensation after only 0.2 seconds had passed. Libet was stumped. How could you be consciously aware of something before your brain had delivered the information to you? He hypothesized that there must be some sort of perceptual mechanism that antedated the signal *in time*. But what *was* this "perceptual mechanism"? The question became a famous bone of contention among neurologists, and continues to be so up to the present day. How is it possible for the brain to "jump time"?

The famous neurologist John C. Eccles said he had the answer. He believed that Libet's "perceptual mechanism" was evidence of an immaterial, self-conscious mind, one that scanned active modules in the brain, getting the jump on the slower processing of the cortex. Other brain processes, he noted, indicated the presence of something that wasn't the product of neurons and electrical-chemical impulses. So in his opinion, the evidence for an immaterial mind was just too overwhelming. In a conversation he had with the philosopher Karl Popper in 1974, he said that he was "constrained to believe there is what we might call a supernatural origin of my unique self-conscious mind." The mind time-travels. Continuously, every moment we are alive, our consciousness is time-lapsed by a tiny, mysterious, 0.2-second journey back in time. Our ability to be in the present moment is more—much more—than it seems to be.

Chapter Five

Star Jelly and Time Cones: The Speed of Time

Time is nature's way to keep everything from happening
at once.
—*John Wheeler*

Last night the angels bent down to earth. There are nights when the heavens seem closer, when gravity holds you just a little less firmly. Last night was one of them. Yesterday afternoon a prairie high blew in from the west, and after a few hours I was sure I could smell yucca and sagebrush. In my garden the peonies bobbed in the gusts. Their ruffled petals fluttered like the organza of debutante dresses as they scattered their perfume on the wind. Above them the trees were restless. I could see the muscled shape of wind gusts moving through the leafy branches. Something in the air elevated my mood. I felt lighter, freer. At dusk a low bank of stratus clouds hovering just above the sunset turned neon pink against a pale turquoise sky, like a Tiepolo fresco. Then, almost as if it had been switched off, the wind died down.

Later, when darkness was firmly established, I went out into the yard again to take a look at the night sky. I was shocked. The night was stuffed with stars. I felt like the only person in an enchanted planetarium, bewitched by the demiurge of night. It was as if another order of darkness had been revealed, as if a layer had been peeled away to reveal a truer darkness, a deeper night, that filled me with dizzy awe. I wondered if the owl I'd seen in March was nearby, sitting on a branch in the secret reaches of night, its eyes sparkling with mystery. The sky was so clear and transparent it seemed that space was somehow closer to the surface of the earth. And everywhere stars. Clusters of stars, necklaces of stars. They sang like destiny in silver notes, and I could see them for what they were—distant, atomic fires of unthinkable immensity, inconceivably remote in time.

Starlight is pure history. Perhaps our earthly time-mosaic, created by the media and architecture, is the natural state of time, like a reflection of the heavens. Perhaps all time—past, present and future—exists at once, everywhere. But the stars take the prize. The night sky contains starlight that started its journey to earth during the Roman era, during the age of dinosaurs, and even from before the earth existed. In the vastness of space, light seems to slow to a crawl, and the vacuum becomes a crystal jelly.

Above my house, Polaris, the pole star, glittered like a fire opal. The luminous gleam from Polaris—the "Pillar of Heaven," as the Greeks called it—took three hundred and sixty years to get here. It appeared to me as it was when the Puritans had just established their first colony in North America. Looking southwest I saw a high, bright star, the fourth-brightest in the sky, Arcturus, only thirty-six light years away. Its light began its interstellar trek to earth during the late 1960s, when NASA manned lunar bases and Woodstock marked the summit of a cultural revolution.

I walked around to the front of my house so that I could see the constellation of Andromeda, below Polaris, where Andromeda's long V just touched the northeastern horizon. Floating just above the constellation was a faint smudge, though its smallness was deceiving. This was the largest single celestial object visible to the naked eye, the galaxy

Andromeda, named after the constellation next to it. Its light began its earthbound journey more than two million years ago, when the first humans, *Homo erectus*, entered Europe from Africa. But there were stars even farther away—stars I could have seen only with the most powerful telescopes on earth—whose glow dates from the beginning of the universe itself. A time wind blows through the heavens.

The strange thing about time and the night sky is that the farther you see into it, the closer you are to the beginning of the universe itself. Because the universe is expanding, wherever we look into the night sky, we look towards a smaller universe. Right now the Hubble Space Telescope can see almost thirteen billion light years back, into a time when the universe was less than a tenth the size it is now. But there is no particular place the telescope has to point to see that far back. No matter where it is aimed, it will see back to the beginning of time. We are surrounded by our beginning—the small has swallowed the huge.

Time Cones

> Henceforth, space by itself, and time by itself, are doomed
> to fade away into mere shadows, and only a kind of union
> of the two will preserve an independent reality.
> —*Hermann Minkowski*

The present is the past's future. The past, as Herman Melville wrote, is the "Future's slave," but the past also shapes the present. No matter how deeply an event is embedded in the past, it opens only towards the future. The fact of its one-time existence, or of its having occurred, gives it a line of history that unfurls before it. Like the cornerstone of a building, each event in the past has a date of appearance, of completion, and then a long tunnel to the present. What did not happen has no tunnel. But there is another dimension of time, one that includes space. All that has happened—the single leaf that fell from a tree two hundred million years ago, the momentary satisfaction of a medieval glazier after installing a pane of glass in Chartres Cathedral—has a special shape in time that was envisaged by two great mathematicians of the early twentieth century.

Whether or not the idea of time as the fourth dimension originated in H. G. Wells' novel *The Time Machine*, it was the Russian mathematician Hermann Minkowski who first put the concept into practice, at the beginning of the twentieth century. He developed a geometry that included time as the fourth dimension, and he was the first person to use the term "space-time," referring to the unified continuum of all four dimensions. We take space-time for granted now, but when it first occurred to Minkowski it was a revolutionary idea. Minkowski realized that everything is moving through time. All things, even things that seem to be unmoving—a pebble sitting on the shore of a lake, an apartment building—are nevertheless in motion. He referred to the line that an object traces through time as a "world line." When two world lines overlap, a meeting in space-time takes place, as when your world line overlaps that of the pebble, should you pick it up from the beach. You plucked it from its unseen path. Seen from this perspective, all things, including ourselves, trail invisible world lines.

A pebble and an apartment building create relatively straight world lines on a four-dimensional graph, but anything moving leaves wiggly lines. What is the shape of a coincidence? In Minkowski's view of space-time, a coincidence would mark a statistically unlikely convergence of world lines—lines crossing great distances of space-time to meet each other. But an uncanny event would be represented by an entirely improbable, extraordinary convergence of world lines. An example of an uncanny event is the case of the Second World War paratrooper whose parachute failed to deploy over enemy territory. He was saved when he miraculously hit the top of a spruce tree at exactly the right point to ensure that each successively larger branch decelerated and cushioned his fall. By the time he hit the bottom branch, he merely slid off it and landed upright, with barely a bruise, in deep snow. That moment changed his life. And he was beyond lucky, as the convergence of world lines that brought about his miracle could statistically never happen again.

Minkowski's theories proved critical for Albert Einstein, whose general theory of relativity hinged on Minkowski's concept of four-dimensional space. Using Minkowskian world lines as a starting point, Einstein came up with an elegant, graphic way to visualize the relationship between time and the speed of light. He knew that light spreads out in a circle from its source, like the ripples from a pebble dropped in a pond. The surface of the pond is the present moment, and each successive moment is a plane just above the first, like a stack of glass sheets. In that stack, the expanding rings, moving upwards with time, create an inverted cone through the vertical time axis. Light in the universe behaves the same way. When a supernova explodes it takes time, even at the speed of light, for the resulting flash to reach other stars and galaxies. Einstein called these expanding world lines "light cones."

The metaphor of the light cone was a tremendous way of unifying the concept of space-time with the way light spreads through the universe. Before the light cone of a distant event arrives, we have no way of knowing what has happened within it, because, in fact, for us it *hasn't* happened. It will only "happen" in earth time when the light reaches us. The edge of a light cone is an expanding "now," trailing the history of the event—the exploding star, the solar flare—behind it. So you could also call them "time cones."

Yet a star doesn't have to explode to create a time cone; anything that happens—a flower opening, a cheque being cashed—produces a virtual time cone, even if the fact isn't relayed at the speed of light. This is because all events and objects affect the things around them. So every world line is nested inside a time cone, and the two of them are tethered together at their beginning. We go on our way through time, creating our world lines, but information about us also spreads over the same period, creating time cones.

All these cones and world lines are oriented in one direction: towards the future. It seems that there *is* a grain, a direction, to time. Time combs through everything, all the world lines, and aligns them towards the future. In that sense history is like hair or fur: it is composed of many individual strands or world lines, and it stands up on end, the way cat fur does when you put a comb charged with static electricity near it, only in this case the static charge is the future. Everything that happened in the past aims towards a future from whose perspective all those things were inevitable, no matter how random or coincidental they were at the time they occurred. Once they happened, they became part of the absolute past, they *did* happen, and the future contains them all. But this knowledge is not like ours, unique and partial; it is the sum total of all that came before. All that has ever happened was necessary to make the present what it is. Our present is the past's future, and the future will eventually contain all presents as pasts when all the time cones finally merge at the end of the universe.

I'd like to think there is a second fur, a second series of time lines that point in the same direction as that of history (as they must), extending not from history towards the present, but from the present towards the future. Because the future isn't real yet, these lines must be virtual. And they are virtual even if, as in the case of repetitive or cyclic phenomena such as sunrises and seasons, the future is almost

100 percent certain. There will always be an element of unpredictability to the future; if the sun is destroyed by a cosmic cataclysm, it may not rise tomorrow. The predictable future, from the vantage of the past, exists solely in the imagination, not in an absolute, universal sense. Yet there it is, nevertheless. Life, consciousness, could be said to be the exception to the present limit of the one-way world lines, for anticipation also seems to create long, thin world lines that extend out of an event in the future towards an individual in the past.

◂ ◂ ◂

Right now I'm constructing my own future world line. I'm planning an excursion, a writing retreat to Cayo Largo, in July. I've been looking at travel brochures and scouting resorts online. Cayo Largo seems to have everything I need: a small, oceanfront hotel complex on an otherwise deserted island, lots of nature, coral reefs and an all-inclusive plan. I've contacted an online travel agency and arranged a fantastic discount. I'll be able to fly down and then work and snorkel for eight days for almost the same amount of money I'd spend during a week at home.

Anticipating a departure date, or any deadline, is a measure of how we experience the passage of time. Right now, my departure is a couple of weeks in the future. It seems distant, almost abstract. Yet I know how quickly the day will come up. Five days before, I will still be calm, unhurried, but four days before, I'll begin to pack and buy the small items I'll need. Anticipation is about waiting. Diane Ackerman described it in *A Natural History of Love*: "The essence of waiting is wishing the future to be in the present. For a slender moment or strings of moments, time does a shadow dance, and the future is roped by the imagination and dragged into the present as if it really were here and now." But then, abruptly, it will be the day before my departure, and all sorts of last-minute errands and untied loose ends will arise: notes to leave for my son, light timers and alarms to set. My anti–time cone will become a bullhorn, barking orders from the future.

Today I bought a small handbook of Spanish phrases. I looked up the Spanish word for "time," *tiempo*. It rang a bell. I've seen it somewhere else recently. On a hunch I went online and revisited a map of Cayo Largo. I scanned the names of beaches and points, and there it was, on the island's southwest tip: Punta mal Tiempo, "Point of Bad Times." The English translation sounded more ominous than the Spanish, which had a more rhythmic, romantic assonance. I wondered what Punta mal Tiempo would look like.

Speaking of Time

Whoever said we have "all the time in the world" wasn't doing last-minute packing while an airport limousine waited outside. What had been "only a matter of time"—my departure date—had arrived "in no time at all." There is no confusing a timeline for one of Minkowski's world lines. My personal timetable was now reduced, I hoped, to being "in the nick of time." As I was throwing a few last items into my suitcase, I realized that these different metaphorical ways of characterizing time represented time's complex and intricate effect on every aspect of our lives.

We often refer to time as if it were a substance, and almost always as a quantity. When we have more than enough, we say that we have "time to spare" or that we have "oodles" of time. For slightly smaller durations we refer to "chunks" of time, as if it were a solid. But we also look at time as having length. If we have a "stretch of time" before us, or a "span," then we can "take our time." Strangely, our relationship to a surplus of time becomes almost predatory. We "kill time" or "waste" it or simply "while it away." But when time begins to "slip away," to "run out" like a fluid, we refer to it as a resource: "time is scarce," there's only a "bit of time," it is "limited." Finally, when we are really "pressed" for time, like grapes in a wine press, or when our time is "up," then it seems that time rises. We say how "time flies" like a bird or an arrow, while an approaching deadline indicates it is "high time."

Everyone knows that time is valuable. You can "buy time" or you can live on "borrowed time." Time can be hoarded or embezzled—you can do things "on your own time" or on "company time"; you can even "spend time"—but, according to folk wisdom, you'll never get "lost time" back again, even if you try to "gain time" elsewhere. "Time hath, my lord, a wallet at his back," said Shakespeare, "wherein he puts alms for oblivion." The old adage has it that "time is money," but even when not exchanged for cash it is "precious," like a jewel. Time is sometimes characterized as an object—you can "find it," and you can "shave off" a little. You can also "make up" some time, as airline pilots are fond of doing.

Romantic time is different. Love will last until "the end of time" or, in the case of stolen love, there will be "time for me and you." The adulterer is said to be "two-timing," and at the beginning of a romance, lovers claim they are having "the time of their lives." Later, when they get older, they recall the "golden times."

For English speakers the progress of time is sometimes militaristic—the "march of time"—while on other occasions it is compared to a fabric or bud that "unfolds." The fabric of time can be sewn: "a stitch in time saves nine." People who look young for their age are said to have kept Father Time "at bay," like an intruder that was fought off. Success against time as an adversary means we have "stood the test of time," while something that outlives many generations, like the "timeless" pyramids, has not only stood the test of time but "stands for all time." Time can be a patron: old customs and institutions we admire are "time-honoured." But as events move deeper into history, things get fuzzy. In the distant past, time becomes granular and semi-opaque. We look back through the "mists of time" to the "dim past," where the "sands of time" lie deep.

Time has many names; in German it is *zeit*—hence *zeitgeist*, the spirit of the times. In Dutch it is *tijd*, reminiscent of "tide," as in "time and tide wait for no man." In reality, the English word *time* does come from the same root as *tide*, at least in Old Norse. In Latin, time was called *tempus*, which in turn was derived from a Greek term that meant "to cut." The Romans, like us, thought of time as something continuous that was apportioned, or "cut," into hours, days, months and years.

◄ ◄ ◄

Around the world there are not only differences in what time is called, there are profound differences in how it is perceived. According to Rafael Núñez, a cognitive scientist from the University of California, San Diego, the Aymara people of the South American Andes, unlike any other language group on earth, think of the past as being in front of them, with the future behind them.

Núñez films his subjects in the field because hand gestures often reveal the underlying way in which the speakers of a particular language metaphorize their world. Núñez noticed that when an Aymara talks about his great-grandparents, he will extend his arm all the way in front of him as he describes them. When he talks about his grandparents he will move his hand a little closer. And when he talks about his parents, he will bring his palm close to his chest. But when asked to talk about future generations he will casually point his thumb over his shoulder.

In Japanese, Hebrew and all the Indo-European languages, including English, as well as languages as different as Polynesian and Bantu, speakers face towards the future. The flow of time streams by them towards the past. Not so for the Aymara, who appear to be unique in their orientation to the past and future. Their word for tomorrow, *q'ipüru*, has a literal meaning of "some day behind one's back." They would agree that time flows, but they look back at the wake of the present like passengers sitting backwards in a motorboat. Because humans share a common perceptual mechanism, our brains have all evolved to recognize the three basic components of time: duration, repetition and simultaneity. All languages express these three aspects of time, as well as the past, present and future. They are embedded in the grammar. And it's at this level that some languages can veer off from each other profoundly.

The language of the Hopi people of the American southwest includes a verb tense not present in other languages. In his seminal 1956 book, *Language, Thought and Reality*, the American linguist Benjamin Lee Whorf called this tense the "active segmentative aspect" because it characterized the action of wavelike or continuously emitted phenomena. In his book he gives the example of the Hopi verb *nö'ya*, which, in its present tense, means "several came out" as referring to persons or objects. But in its segmentative form, the verb becomes *nöya'yata*, which means "it is coming out in successive multitudes, gushing or spraying out," like water coming out of a fountain. The segmentative form allows a very precise description of moving liquids or particles. Whorf felt that this new verb form allowed the Hopi to understand certain phenomena in a deeper way than we do, and he recommended that young physicists study Hopi, perhaps even learn it, in order to better conceptualize the elusive nature of quantum physics, a science that characterizes the universe in terms of particles and waves.

Formal Italian has three past tenses with progressively deeper levels of historical depth: the recent past, or *trapassuto prossimo*; the middle past, or past perfect, a long time ago; and the *passato remoto*, referring to events from quite a long time ago, at least hundreds of years. Dante's *La divina commedia* was written in the *passato remoto*. In English there is the wonderful past pluperfect, denoting an action completed before a particular past point in time—"I had seen the owl before spring arrived." It is the verbs, in all languages, that mediate the influence of time on our lives. By contrast, most nouns are almost entirely timeless, except when they refer to *elements* of time such as sundials, hours, schedules or seasons. (But time must be on our minds a lot. According to the Oxford English Corpus, *time* tops the list of the most common nouns in the English language.) And the only proper nouns we have for time, aside from noon and midnight, are dates. A phrase like "8:46 a.m., September 11, 2001," sounds abstract, but it is a name for a particular point in time that everyone knows. Adjectives and adverbs can share properties of either realm, time or space: a car can move quickly, but it can also be shiny. Ultimately, it is the sum of all levels of metaphor and grammar that define the true relationship of any given language-speaking group to time.

Tasting Time

But for all these characterizations of time, the qualities of time still elude me. What are they? What is time itself? What does it feel like? Could something like time, which is more ineffable than a vacuum, have any qualities at all? Even a vacuum, the absolute absence of anything, can be sealed inside a box, confined to a place. Time cannot. Colourless, odourless, tasteless, without shape, form or substance, it nevertheless shapes, directs and contains us. As an exercise I asked a dozen friends and acquaintances to imagine that they could grasp a handful of time. What would it sound like? I asked. Or look, feel, smell, even taste like?

There were some consistencies. As to colour, four of them agreed that time was blue, or silver-blue, though there was little agreement after that. Some of their colour associations were poetic—time was "the colour of diamonds underwater," or "the amber of a nocturnal animal's eyes." Several people also agreed on the feel of time—one saying that it would feel like an oyster on the tongue and another that it would be slippery and shiny, while still another claimed that time would feel oily, or "slitherly." A friend who refused to participate because he said he disdained synesthetic associations did mention that time sounded like a large highway from a distance. To others it sounded like the rustle of leaves or the ultrasonic calls of bats.

As to taste, well, there was hardly any agreement: saltpetre and wine, metal, Szechwan pepper sauce, capers. But it was the *smell* of time that seemed to have the most personal associations. It smelled like a cold, snowy day or burnt ants or elementary school cloakrooms. Everyone I asked had very private, idiosyncratic associations that were as varied as their personalities. At the personal level, time is as intimate and complex as the individual who perceives it.

As for me, I imagine that time would smell like Tutankhamen's tomb when it was first opened in 1923. I imagine that attics and unused closets, like briefer versions of Tutankhumen's tomb, also have the smell of time to them. These closed spaces are time capsules where months, sometimes years, pass before they are opened again. The air must have a scent of time, something above the vapours rising from the partially abandoned or rarely used objects, the camping equipment and fans, the old Halloween costumes. The interior of a closet, the disposition of the articles placed by whoever put them there, remains unchanged as all else changes. Neighbours move away, children grow up, but these things stay the same. Sometimes a decade can pass before you revisit the attic or storage space to get an old photo album or a family game. It is here, when you first open the door, that you can smell time. A time traveller has been here—yourself, when you were a little younger, perhaps a little stronger, and perhaps (you realize with some poignancy) a little more optimistic.

Chapter Six

Time, Space and Eternity

Eternity.
It is the sea mingled
with the sun.
—*Arthur Rimbaud*

When Arthur Rimbaud wrote those lines in *Une saison en enfer* in 1873, he was only nineteen years old, yet he already had an old soul, old enough to see eternity dance in sunlight on waves. For Rimbaud, the motion of those sun-dazzled waves contained a hypnotic secret, not just the fusion of particle and wave, of flow and time, but also a special emptiness that echoed something in his soul. He wasn't the first poet to equate infinity with sunlight. In the fifth century B.C., the Greek poet Aeschylus described a similar oceanic vista in *Prometheus Bound* as the "myriad laughter of the ocean waves."

◂ ◂ ◂

I can't claim to have seen eternity in a sunny ocean, but I have seen moonlight on waves at night. A more subtle spectacle, perhaps, and yet completely mesmerizing. It was years ago. I was alone in northern Ontario, on a high rock overlooking a remote lake on a summer night. The stone was still warm to the touch from the heat of the day, though it was close to midnight. A full moon had just risen and it hung over the water. There was a breeze, enough to raise small waves, so the reflection of the moon in the lake laid a dazzling path to the far shore.

I stared at that shimmering corridor for half an hour, entranced. I lost myself in a kind of reverie, and as I did the reflections on the waves transformed themselves from dancing water into a glittering loom of sparkles and points of light. I lost track of time, *and* perspective. There were moments when I seemed to be looking at a vertical, flashing tapestry of lights that could have been electric, they were so quick, so precise and myriad. Eventually it seemed I was looking into the heart of some vast, nocturnal computer making innumerable calculations of cosmic equations. I was outside of time and space for that half-hour, and when I finally, regretfully, left the spectacle, I was almost dizzy with what my eyes had drunk in.

◂ ◂ ▸

There is a reason why light has such mesmeric power—it is beyond time. All light is, even the light from a firefly, or a candle. Light moves at 186,281 miles per second—which, as Einstein discovered, is the ultimate velocity in the universe. But Einstein discovered something else about light, something extraordinary, which is that the closer something gets to the speed of light, the slower its "on-board" time proceeds relative to the rest of us. When that object reaches the speed of light, its time-warp factor (the amount by which its on-board time slows relative to the rest of the universe) reaches infinity. In other words, for something travelling at the speed of light, time freezes.

But it gets stranger. There are other effects of time warp that don't require reaching the speed of light, effects that show just how "local" time really is. Imagine twins. One twin leaves earth for twenty years in a spaceship that approaches the speed of light. The other stays behind.

When the space-travelling twin returns, she will have aged much less than her sister has. If her spaceship travelled at 86 percent of the speed of light and she left earth in the year 2,000 for twenty years, upon her return she will have aged a mere ten years, while her twin will have aged twenty. Also, her on-board calendars will show the year to be 2010, not 2020. That's because, for the space-bound twin, only ten years did elapse. But her time went more slowly relative to the earthbound twin. The only two "simultaneous" times that they will both be able to agree on will be the arrival and departure dates in earth time: otherwise they'll have completely different, and relative, time experiences.

Einstein once put his theory of time warp in more prosaic language for a reporter. He said, "When you are courting a nice girl an hour seems like a second. When you sit on a red-hot cinder a second seems like an hour. That's relativity!" In other words, the "local" time for each twin was like the "subjective" time in Einstein's analogy. You might object that there is a universal, fixed time relative to both their time-lines, but, according to Einstein, there isn't.

This is because of the fixed velocity of light. If the spaceship the travelling twin took was moving at 86 percent of the speed of light and it flashed a light ahead of it, that light would not include the speed of the spaceship—it would still move at 186,281 miles per second! Imagine an Olympic javelin thrower. He runs as he throws the javelin to boost its speed; his velocity is added to the javelin's velocity. But if he were throwing a light beam instead, it wouldn't matter if he ran, stood still, or walked backwards—the light-javelin would still travel at exactly the same speed. It's all very counterintuitive, even to scientists.

◂ ◂ ◂

So where does the added velocity of light go? Time. Which is why the faster the spaceship goes, the more time slows down on board relative to the rest of us. And here is where things get weird. Since time-dilation effects occur when objects are travelling at appreciable fractions of the speed of light, even the electrons orbiting the nuclei of heavy metals create time-dilation effects. Scientists have suggested that the colour of gold is not due to the pigment of the metal itself. Its glitter is produced by the relativistic effects of the speed of its electrons circling the gold atoms within the metal. Gold's very substance is slightly out of synch with our time, and that slight difference creates its lustre. But the electrons in gold move at a snail's pace compared to those in masses of pure uranium, some of which move incrementally faster than the speed of light. The time warp causes nuclear fuel rods stored at the bottom of heavy-water pools to glow an unearthly blue. The glow is called "Cherenkov radiation," after the physicist who discovered it.

Gravity fields also stretch time, the reason being that, in the final scheme of things, gravity is equivalent to constant acceleration. The greater the gravity at the surface of a planet or star, the more time is slowed down. If you could survive standing on the surface of a neutron star (one of the densest objects known to exist), the universe that you saw around you would be billions of years younger than the one we see. Even on a smaller body, like our earth, there is a measurable difference in the flow of time in the upper atmosphere and the surface of the earth. This was proven conclusively in 1976, when two scientists from the Smithsonian Astrophysical Observatory, Robert Vessot and Martin Levine, synchronized two hydrogen maser clocks and rocketed one of them fifty miles above the earth. They discovered, with an accuracy of seventy parts in a million, that time was flowing slightly faster fifty miles above the earth than on its surface.

There are even stronger gravitational fields among the stars. The most massive of these are adjacent to black holes. If a space traveller could hover just outside a black hole and video conference with someone on earth, both space traveller and earthling would be able to see the effects of gravity/time dilation. On the space traveller's screen, the earthling would seem to be hyper-animated, like a film on fast-forward. Even his voice would be high and squeaky. On the earthling's screens, the space traveller would appear to be moving in slow motion, his voice low and distorted. But what would happen if the space traveller's engines failed and he fell into the black hole, and, as he did so, he looked back at the universe? What he would see would be time outside the black hole speeded up fantastically. He would see the universe expanding and see galaxies spinning like Catherine wheels while stars whizzed by. Some stars he would see explode and wink out, while still others would be sucked into black holes. And just as he fell into oblivion, if he was lucky, he'd see the universe beginning to fade into nothingness. As Paul Davies wrote in *The Last Three Minutes*, his book about the end of the universe, "A black hole is a little region of space that contains the end of time."

STOPPING TIME

Today, a clear, sunny summer day, I tried to imagine what it would be like if time stopped. At first I imagined the whole world frozen, like statuary—the rustling of the leaves of the tree in my front yard rendered completely still, as if transposed into a museum diorama, that car turning the corner also arrested, the faint blue cloud of exhaust hovering motionless at the end of the tailpipe. I realized that my body, too, could not be immune from this spell. I'd be frozen like the leaves and the car and I would stare out of myself like some sort of conscious statue. Following the fantasy further, I realized that if time had really stopped, I wouldn't be able to move my eyes. "So, I couldn't look around. Big deal," I thought. I could still enjoy the scene my eyes had fixed on, couldn't I? But then it struck me that if time had stopped, how could it still be running in my mind? How could I have thoughts? How could impulses still be moving along the nerves in my brain? Like the Greeks, who attributed rational thought to Cronos, I understood that thought would be impossible. Time, and any sort of awareness, would cease.

And then it occurred to me that time *could* stop, and restart a little later, and we'd never know it. We are so completely enmeshed in time that if it stopped we'd have no way of knowing that it had. I had another idea. What if time *was* stopping every once in a while? Perhaps time isn't a continuous flow, but a series of stops and starts. Time could stop for a few seconds, or even a thousand years, and within that timeless period we'd be like unconscious statues—the car forever turning the corner, the motionless leaves. Would beings from other time dimensions take tours through our world to gawk at us?

I wondered if, as David Finkelstein's speculations about chronons suggest, time wasn't like the quanta in quantum physics, where light and mass come in small, discrete units that are neither waves nor particles, but something else, like mathematical points. Perhaps time unfolds in quantum pulses, and between each pulse it stops, though these "time stoppages" might be so short in duration that they would be undetectable, even if we had some way of detecting them. Our equipment, of course (at least according to my fantasy), also being operated by time, would likewise be oblivious to having been "outside" of time.

So then I asked myself, what if the whole universe were linked to this quantum pulse of time-on, time-off, like a cosmic, universal clock ticking? In other words, what if everything in the universe stopped and started, in a sense disappearing and reappearing like a stroboscopic light that used matter instead of light? Would this pulse transcend local time and become a sort of universal time? If it were 2:00 p.m. "universal time" on earth, would it also be 2:00 p.m. "universal time" on Proxima Centauri, the closest star to the sun, 4.22 light years distant? I'd like to think so.

It's appealing to imagine that someone on Proxima Centauri could look at a clock, or however they measure their time, and say, "Right now, on earth, someone is also looking at a clock, even though we are light years apart." This sense of a universal time—an omniscient and ever-present moment continuous throughout the universe—is more like a belief than a possibility. It is the closest thing I have to an article of faith, an idea of God. If a super-being tapped into such a universal time, that being would know what was going on in all parts of the universe in a simultaneity that transcended the speed of light. A "now" that was everywhere.

But that is impossible. Unfortunately for my fantasy, and as we have seen, Albert Einstein proved that a universal "now" is impossible, that "now" is totally local and relative. Einstein believed in God, but probably not one that could know everything. Relative velocities and the speed of light are absolute limits, and it turns out that light is the closest we can get to that absolute, the infinite. Miraculously, we are bathed in it every day. So what would it be like to move at the speed of light, to be a photon—half wave, half particle—slipping through space on your way to infinity? What would time be like for it?

From light's perspective, the universe it illuminates is continuously changing like a time-lapse film. In fact, it looks very much like the view our unfortunate astronaut had as he passed through the outer edge of the black hole. Stars are born, age and explode in minutes. Spinning galaxies collide and recede dizzily into space.

But "on board" the photon, time has stopped, and all this vast commotion of stars and galaxies is taken into its timeless heart. As the

Australian astrophysicist Paul Davies writes, "At the speed of light itself, time stands still." Light is a strange thing. It somehow exists outside of time yet within it. Perhaps that's why sunlight, the strongest source of light we know, seems filled with nostalgia, at least for poets. It pines for a universe it can never touch, even as it warms and illuminates it. Its destiny is eternity, slipping ahead of everything on its one-way journey, at the speed limit of the universe, to the edge of time.

ETERNITY

> It is eternity now. I am in the midst of it. It is about me in
> the sunshine; I am in it, as the butterfly in the light-laden
> air. Nothing has to come; it is now. Now is eternity; now
> is the immortal life.
> —*Richard Jefferies*, The Story of My Heart

I landed in Cayo Largo yesterday, in the middle of a tropical storm. It was the afternoon of the first Saturday in July. Just before landing, the jet emerged out of low clouds and, as it descended, cruised over fifty miles of small keys and reefs. The coral lagoons studded the shallow, blue-green ocean like precious stones, and I could imagine snorkelling through each and every one of them. "Let me off here!" I thought. With a parachute, snorkel, mask and flippers, I would have all I needed.

After the plane landed and we disembarked, the first rush of Caribbean air at the door of the airplane submerged me in an element midway between liquid and air. My light cotton pants and T-shirt immediately felt like hot flannel. The tarmac was wet, and the rain-slicked fan palms semaphored in the wind beside the entrance to the small terminal. By the time I'd got to the hotel and had eaten dinner, it was dark. Lightning flickered around the open-air dining room, though by the time I returned to my room to sleep, the rain had stopped.

◆ ◆ ◆

This morning the sky is perfectly clear and the ocean still. After breakfast I go searching for a reef and find one—a long streak of dark blue-green against the pale turquoise of the ocean—close to shore at the north end of the resort's beach. It's high tide, and the low swells are just cresting over the coral. I hurry back to my room, grab my snorkel and flippers, and within minutes I'm floating over paradise.

There are all my old friends—the sergeant major fish, the psychedelic parrotfish and serene schools of blue tangs. Like a crown jewel, a queen triggerfish swims by, its flagrantly tropical body adorned with electric-blue flashes. Below, the fantastic shapes of brain coral, staghorn coral and sea fans spike up. I can hear the reef tick, like an irregular clock, as the parrotfish and wrasse forage through the coral, picking at it with their beaks. This ubiquitous tinkling and clicking, like rolling cinders, seems a curiously dry noise for such a submerged world.

And everywhere there's life, floating and profligate. In the sky above me, frigate birds drift, their own medium a blue fluid quicker than water. But it's the wind and waves that stir it all. Occasionally the backwash from a big wave creates undertow that spills tangs, trumpetfish and gobies over the brain coral at the reef's edge and into the blue depths beyond the drop-off. This spur-and-groove reef has been formed by thousands of years of waves, and the sand flats between the coral chimneys seem unchanged since the Devonian period. Everything, including me, rocks in slow circles with the waves, like riders on a bus swaying in unison with the curves of the road. We roll together in the subsurface squeeze and flow of swells, a confederacy of helpless, living jelly in the ocean.

After an hour or so I return to my room, lie down on my bed in the air-conditioned coolness. I can still feel the ocean swells in my body. I drift off. When I awake it's just after four o'clock in the afternoon. I pull back the curtains and I know, as soon as I see the light on the yellow stucco walls of the adjacent building, that this is the time. Each island in the Caribbean has its own hour of eternity, a signal hour that epitomizes the endless summer of the tropics. In Bonaire it arrives around five or six in the afternoon, as the sun angles low. In Cozumel it happens later, just before sundown. On Cayo Largo I am surprised to see it arriving so early.

I go out onto the balcony, and the surging heat is another surprise. The sun is lower in the sky. The light is a slightly diminished tropical sunlight, the stunned opulence of permanent heat, that is tempered just enough to bring out the infinity of time locked in its beams. I see it most clearly in the shining highlights on the fronds of the coconut palms outside my second-floor balcony. Their improbably large pinnate leaves rustle in a vague breeze. Behind them, the ocean, the orange and yellow rustic villas and the infinite blue of the sky, holding a single frigate bird that hovers above the dunes, are like a picture of themselves. Time stands still for an hour, and in that brief, extravagant, all-encompassing eternity there is a humming abundancy, a poignancy that saturates the sunlight and the palms.

BEYOND TIME

The idea of eternity has excited, terrified and inspired people since the beginning of civilization, and probably before that. Over the millennia we have discovered two kinds of eternity: one an endless period of time, an infinity; the other timelessness, a special state with no future or past, only an infinite present. Of the two, the second must be closest to the real eternity, because if there is a past and a future, no matter how long their duration, there must also have been a beginning, and there must also be an end. Right now, our universe is still relatively young at 13.7 billion years, and you could argue that the lifespan of the universe might as well represent an eternity, since the ultimate length of its existence—billions upon billions of years—is beyond individual comprehension. We can know these numbers, but we cannot *feel* them the way we do a normal lifespan. As the old Jamaican saying goes, "Who feels it, knows it." The longest time we can know in a human lifetime is a century, though the only centenarian of my acquaintance says she feels like she's lived an eternity.

If we aren't able to experience real eternity, at least the eternity of duration, we can at least experience more immediate eternities. In his *Tractatus Logico-philosophicus*, Ludwig Wittgenstein wrote, "If we take eternity to mean not infinite temporal duration but timelessness, then eternal life belongs to those who live in the present." Like Zen monks do. When the owl enthralled me in March, I was so completely in the moment that I experienced a flash of what felt like Zen eternity. But not all experiences of infinitude are such revelations. There are banal eternities too—the red light that never turns green, the bank lineup where time stands still, the Internet download that doesn't end. Although frustrating, and boring, these moments can be almost as intense an experience of time standing still as emotional epiphany is.

◢ ◢ ◢

The mystic sense of time standing still is intrinsically more interesting and almost always more spiritual. In his 1929 Gifford Lecture, Ernest Barnes, an Anglican bishop and physicist, recounted a profound experience of eternity during a walk to a beach on the coast of England.

"I remember," he said, "that I was going to bathe from a stretch of shingle to which the few people who stayed in the village seldom went. Suddenly the noise of the insects was hushed. Time seemed to stop. A sense of infinite power and peace came upon me. I can best liken the combination of timelessness with amazing fullness of existence to the feeling one gets in watching the rim of a great silent fly-wheel or the unmoving surface of a deep, strongly flowing river. Nothing happened: yet existence was completely full. All was clear."

The crucial image in Barnes's vision is his metaphor of the flywheel. Large, spoked iron wheels, often twenty feet in diameter and weighing several tons, flywheels were used to drive machinery in the industrial era. Their flat outer rims were so precisely machined that, if you ignored the whirring spokes, you saw hardly any difference between a moving flywheel and one that had stopped. Barnes's metaphor is excellent, for you can touch the rim as it moves and feel the surface slipping by under your finger, as I once did on a public-school class trip to an industrial museum in Greenfield, Michigan. But he gives us another metaphor, just to nail it—this time, of a river. Again, immense power and movement with a deceptively calm surface. It is as if, standing still, he had witnessed the flow of time itself as it whirred past him.

◂ ◂ ◂

Barnes's experience of eternity is altogether different from the eternity of the monotheistic religions, most notably Christianity, which hold out the promise of an actual, durational eternity in an afterlife. Many religious writers have talked about this, though none so eruditely, to my mind at least, as Benedict Spinoza, the Dutch philosopher. According to Spinoza, who was a pantheist, "God and all the attributes of God are eternal." He goes on to say that since we are one with God, "We feel and know that we are eternal." His certainty came from philosophical knowledge and spiritual conviction, though it is hard to say how literally he took the notion of eternity in an afterlife.

◂ ◂ ◂

When I was young and had trouble getting to sleep, my mind would drift towards strangely cosmic themes. I would grow very anxious and claustrophobic when I thought about life and the fact that we die. I'd try to temper the idea of mortality with that of eternity, which was certainly preferable. But then I found myself imagining what it would be like to exist forever—unchanging, infinite existence would be just as intolerable—and I'd get existential agoraphobia, fear of wide-open spaces. Both alternatives seemed equally frightening. As Joseph Addison, the English essayist and poet, put it in 1713, "Eternity! Thou pleasing, dreadful thought!"

Years later it occurred to me that there might be a solution—two solutions, in fact—to the potential agony of eternal existence. The first was to exist completely in the moment, unaware of past or future. That way, the prospect of an interminable infinity in front of you could be avoided. The other solution was to constantly transform yourself. If you gradually changed, becoming in effect someone else, then you could easily cope with eternal existence because you would be a series of different beings, none of them technically immortal. I would choose the first, though in daily life I manage to live it only in rare moments.

There is something of the eternal, also, in romantic love. At its heart it is immortal, and, like life itself, love seems confined by the limits of mortality—it can easily last a lifetime. As the English poet John Donne wrote, "Love, all alike, no season knows, nor clime, / Nor hours, days, months, which are the rags of time." In so much romantic art, music and literature, the abiding theme involves love that will last till the end of time, that will stay true forever. In *Antony and Cleopatra*, Shakespeare evoked this theme when he wrote, "Eternity was in our lips and eyes, / Bliss in our brows bent." It is as if the strength and purity of the lovers' emotions transcended time itself—though time is both an ally and an enemy of lovers. When lovers are apart, the minutes crawl by, but when they finally unite, time takes on another aspect altogether—their sojourn in bliss is not measured by the clock. Eternity burnishes their bodies; it is the streaming pulse of their passion, their longing.

◂ ◂ ◂

My week in Cayo Largo ended too quickly, even if time stood still for one enchanted hour every afternoon. And a week is hardly an eternity, though time *did* pass differently for me there, almost as if I were one of the relativistic twins. My seven-day idyll felt more like two weeks than one, so that on my return yesterday evening it seemed I had been away longer. But here's the relativistic effect: I phoned my next-door neighbour who'd agreed to look after my house while I was away. "Are you back already?" he said. Obviously, for him, it seemed like less than a week had passed.

Apparently the formation of new memories does, in fact, alter our sense of the passage of time. Dinah Avni-Babad, a psychologist at the Hebrew University in Jerusalem, has studied the relationship between habit, memory and time and has found that in our routine existence we operate out of habit, as if we are on autopilot. Time passes more quickly for us because everything we do is repeated daily. We don't form new memories. But new experiences form new memories that, from a subjective viewpoint, expand the sense of time. So if you want to live longer, or at least have the experience of it, you should shake up your routine. Get away if you can. I recommend Cayo Largo.

◂ ◂ ◂

Late this afternoon I sat on my patio, enjoying the lushness of my garden. In the centre of my yard there's a potted fan palm—a washingtonia— that's too big for the house. I board it every winter at a greenhouse, and its return to my yard each spring is an occasion. Last month it was delivered by two men and a truck. The palm in its oversize terracotta pot instantly became, as it always does, the tropical focus of the yard. The tomato plants and basil were well started and the rhododendron was still flowering. The slanting sun spotlighted my new banana tree, which, according to a little label hung on one leaf, is a new species that is winter-hardy if it's cut back and mulched. We'll see. My yard is a small, tropical oasis that harks back to Cayo Largo, though I miss the saturated tropical sun and the late-afternoon peek into eternity.

And yet the yellow roses by my patio were blooming mightily and there was a poignancy to the late-afternoon sunlight. The rose blossoms. Above and behind them, plumed thunderheads glowed pink on the horizon, echoing the shapes of the oak trees. Eternal in its transience, infinite in its uniqueness, my garden was a still life, a tableau flooded with cosmic nostalgia. The partially opened rose and the other one that was already losing its petals . . . that particular scene would never occur again in the whole existence of the universe. It was bookended by eternity.

Chapter Seven

Shaping Time

Time is at the heart of all that is important to human beings.
—*Bernard d'Espagnat*

We should not say that one man's hour is worth another man's hour, but rather that one man during an hour is worth just as much as another man during an hour. Time is everything, man is nothing: he is at the most time's carcass.
—*Karl Marx*

Janus of Now

This morning I had a claustrophobic experience, probably because my sense of time's passage has been heightened lately. I've become disturbingly aware of how quickly the present recedes into the past. What happened was, I was listening to music on my computer and watching the cursor that shows what part of the song is playing, when it struck me that the cursor was a metaphor for my own existence. But with two big differences: I didn't know how long my "music" would last, and I couldn't click and drag my location in time forwards or backwards.

Then I realized there was another difference, and this is where my sense of claustrophobia was centred. "Now," our personal black dot, is a fixative. Its trailing edge instantly freezes the movements of whatever action is surfing in from the future on the wave of the present. As narrow as "now" is—and it *is* narrow—it still has two sides, one closed, the other open. Its trailing side closes off all possibility of change, while its forward, future-facing edge allows *all* change. The universe and everything in it are like angels dancing on the head of this pin. All that moves—planets, butterflies, soccer games, dozing monkeys, ballerinas and aging wine—becomes instantly locked into permanent, sculptural history by the freezing action of the trailing edge of the past.

And then another possibility occurred to me and reversed all my notions about the direction of time. Maybe, I thought, the direction of the flow *isn't* from the future into the past. What if "now," the present moment, is a membrane pushed upwards on the surface of an expanding past, which, as it blossoms towards the future, crystallizes everything that occurs? Any way you look at it, it seems that movement is a miracle. There's so little time in the present moment. How does anything happen at all if "now" is so fleeting, especially if it is so much less than we could possibly know?

◂ ◂ ◂

St. Augustine pondered time mightily. He too, as we saw earlier, was preoccupied by the riddle of the present. In his *Confessions*, he wrote, "How can the past and future be when the past no longer is and the future is not yet? As for the present, if it were always present and never moved on to become the past, it would not be time but eternity." Here again, eternity seems to flower out of the present, "every instant of time, a pin-prick of eternity," as the enlightened emperor Marcus Aurelius wrote in *Meditations*. Yet still, it seems to me that "now" is a like a thin plane that the future passes through, transforming as it flows past the present into the unmoving past. Or maybe "now" is more like an incredibly fast construction crew building a high-rise. As they climb into nothingness, they leave a concrete building behind. Or do they? From our perspective, riding along with the construction and confined only to the present, the building might as well disappear beneath us as it's being constructed. We'll never take the elevator down—or up, for that matter.

But if the past and the future exist at once, as the physicists say, then perhaps the present is only the illusion of movement, like a laser light show at a dance club. As the laser slices the smoke in cross-section, new, convoluted landscapes are revealed, the very same way that the future seems to unfold. It's all very perplexing. Maybe I should adopt the English essayist Charles Lamb's attitude. In a letter he sent to Thomas Manning on a cold winter day in January 1810, he wrote, "Nothing puzzles me more than time and space; and yet nothing troubles me less, as I never think about them."

▲ ▲ ▲

Yesterday I decided to lie on a towel in my backyard and sunbathe. It was a hot, mid-July afternoon, and cicadas rasped their shimmering songs in the trees. I figured I'd sun myself for a half-hour, and, since I wanted to tan evenly, I knew I'd have to turn over at least once in that time, after fifteen minutes. But that would neglect my sides. If I divided the fifteen-minute periods in half, I would be able to devote equal time to my whole body. But here is where division of the hour into sixty minutes breaks down, since fifteen minutes cannot be divided evenly. Half of fifteen minutes is seven and a half minutes, and half of seven and a half minutes is three and three-quarters. I lay on my stomach pondering the math of this odd little corner of horology, when my thoughts were derailed by a new vista—my view, just above the level of the grass, went along the length of the yard to the garage. I was in the world of insects.

A big blue dragonfly sunned itself on a rock to my left in the garden. I was close enough to see that its transparent wings were minutely interlaced with dark veins, like miniature stained-glass windows. Everywhere on the lawn, pollen-dusted bees were visiting clover flowers, and several iridescent green flies with impossibly long, angled legs, were sunning on blades of grass. I saw an ant carrying a winged seed twice its size. At the ant's scale, the grass might as well have been a bamboo jungle. It tugged purposefully at its load and kept a remarkably straight path through the grass. Just then, a trio of small insects—flies or wasps, I couldn't tell—flew over my head from behind me and zoomed at grass-tip level towards the garage. They were going so quickly I could barely track them, and it was only because they were flying down the axis of my perspective that I could see what they were up to. All three were tumbling through the air like miniature jet fighters. They hovered and plunged and dove at each other like tiny top guns as they rocketed forwards. The whole nimble flyover must have taken only half a second, and then they vanished.

To them I must have seemed as slow as an elephant or a beached whale, and I couldn't help but imagine that their relative time frame was much, much faster than mine. Those flies seemed like aerial Femtonians. Whenever an animal is fast, you can bet that neurons, the communicative cells that make up our own nervous system and brain, are involved. Plants, which have no neurons, are some of the slowest organisms on the planet. Worms, with their basic nervous systems, are speed demons compared to plants, but arthropods, particularly insects, are very fast. In terms of manoeuvrability, speed and complexity, evolution hasn't really improved too much on insects. Even the mongoose, which can outrace the cobra's strike, has difficulty snatching a fly out of the air.

◂ ◂ ◂

If speed depends on neurons, then mammals must be the speediest animals of all. And in a way, they are. A cat may not have quicker reactions than a fly, but it uses its additional neurons to predict where the fly will go and intercepts it there. Mammals can be extraordinarily fast. A bat can fly through the whirling blades of a fan, and a cheetah can sprint at over sixty miles per hour. We humans are not as fast as cheetahs, or as agile as bats, but we don't have to be. Our brains have the most effective concentration of neurons in the animal kingdom. There are other mammals with bigger brains and more neurons—elephants and dolphins, to name two—but human brains seem to be more efficiently interconnected. They allow us to think ahead, to take duration and speed one step faster. They allow us to collapse time.

◂ ◂ ◂

We are beings who stand outside and within time. Time is our tool and our medium. No other living thing measures and calculates it so precisely as we do. Even before clocks, we knew, by observing the cyclical patterns of the seasons, exactly when to plant our crops, when to harvest, when to prepare for winter weather. By anticipating the future as well as holding on to our past with stories and monuments, we exist outside of the present moment, the moment in which most animals live out their lives. Despite the fact that some of the most spiritually enlightened religions on the planet admonish us to spend more time in the present moment, not existing in the present moment is an intrinsically human trait, at least since we have become technological. We use time like a map; we can point to where we have been and we can plan where we are going. We are cartographers of time. Ever since the advent of language, storytellers have transported us to the past, and soothsayers, like reconnaissance scouts, have glimpsed the future.

But if we are creatures of time, we are also slaves to it. When we began to allocate time, time became an obstacle between us and our desires. Many of the tasks that we perform every day seem tedious because they take so much time. I never have enough of it. I'm always five minutes late for appointments, I'm continually juggling time between my children, friends, errands, chores and deadlines. To top it all off, lately I've been neglecting to put on my wristwatch. It feels like a slave-band, or like the radio anklets that prisoners on restricted parole have to wear. And there are always the tedious little routines that have to be repeated every day—dressing and undressing, opening and closing drawers, putting out and putting away dishes. I find flossing and brushing my teeth at the end of the evening a monumentally dreary business.

To rein in my impatience, I sometimes imagine a parallel life in a community on the edge of the Sahara Desert. There, I live in a small village where each day I have to trek an hour and a half in the hot sun to a water well. At the well I fill four five-gallon plastic containers and then carry them back at the ends of long poles perched on my shoulders. Many times along the way, I'm forced to put down the load and massage my aching shoulders. Compared to those three imagined hours spent on such a menial task, the actual five minutes I have to spend in a bank lineup seem like nothing.

Yet psychological studies of people of limited means living in Third World countries report them as being generally happier. How is it that a culture without all the time-saving devices we have—the washing machines, acronyms, keyboard commands, dishwashers, time-sharing and multi-tasking—end up having more time for family and being more content? There's a kind of law at work here, something like the law of income and spending: no matter how high your income, your spending will always rise to equal it. We use our time savers not to create leisure time but to fit in even more appointments, more cellphone calls, more résumé updates, more appointments, more professional-development seminars, more time spent listening to the menu options on automated phone services, scanning electronics manuals or downloading software upgrades, movies and music.

◂ ◂ ◂

At a dinner party the other night, a friend told me that time seemed to be going faster. Things he used to have time for a couple of years ago were now rushed. "Time's speeding up," he said. I've experienced the same thing. Some days time is sluggish, other days it's fast. But, of course, time can't speed up or slow down, at least for us, here on planet earth. Certainly there are places in the universe where time is quicker or slower than the average, but here it's pretty consistent. Anyway, even if time *were* faster or slower, we'd never know it because local time always flows at the same rate relative to itself. If time seemed to be going faster for my friend, it could only be because he was slowing down. I said to my friend, "It isn't time speeding up, it's us slowing down."

William S. Burroughs, the American beat writer, would have disagreed with me. He claimed to have experienced a quantitative alteration of time in the mid-1950s, while he was in Tangiers writing *Naked Lunch*. Upon his arrival in Tangiers he rented an apartment, and by the middle of the first year he had fallen into a schedule that persisted throughout his time there. He rose late and had his breakfast, then visited a few local shops to buy necessities and food. After stocking his apartment he had coffee or an early-afternoon drink at one of the many cafés in Tangiers. In the evenings he wrote. This routine was interrupted once a month by an afternoon visit to the American Express office, where Burroughs' family stipend was waiting for him. He would get there well before the office closed to collect his money.

As the years passed, Burroughs claimed that he noticed a disturbing trend. Although his routine remained constant—he got up at the same time, he did his errands as usual—the afternoons seemed to go faster. This trend continued until, one day, he arrived at the American Express office and it was closed. Looking at his watch, he was amazed to see that it was already after 5:00 p.m. What had happened to the time? The leisurely pace of his afternoons had been taken from him. Increasingly, it seemed that he had to rush through his errands; he barely had time to shop before the stores closed. What was going on?

He came up with an ingenious explanation. He claimed that an alien civilization, whose sun was about to explode and destroy its home planet, had discovered a way of sucking time from other regions of the universe in order to buy more for itself. Looking deep into space, the aliens discovered earth, fat with excess time. They began siphoning off our hours just after Burroughs moved to Tangiers. No wonder his days felt shorter. (My guess is that his heroin addiction slowed him down a little, but you have to give him points for a great alibi.)

◂ ◂ ◂

I have my own problems. Try as I might, I cannot get out of my house sooner than two hours after I wake up. Other people don't need this much time, so I decided to write down my morning schedule and analyze why it takes me so long. I usually get up at 8:30 a.m., turn down my sheets to air them, put on a pair of shorts and a T-shirt, then wash my face and shave. That takes twelve minutes. By 8:42 I'm downstairs. I open the blinds, look in the mailbox and go to the kitchen. Two minutes. Eight forty-four finds me drinking orange juice and putting away last night's dishes. Now it's 8:52. I listen to my phone messages. Three minutes, unless I have to answer one immediately.

For the next twelve minutes I prepare breakfast: a bowl of cereal with fresh slices of banana and mango. I also put coffee and some water into the coffee maker. But I don't eat breakfast right away. I eat it after my exercises. At 9:06 I'm doing stretches and weights in the living room. Six minutes. Then I finish my juice, take some vitamins and go jogging. My route winds through a neighbourhood park and several blocks around my house. Fifteen minutes. At 9:32 I start the coffee maker, go upstairs, shower, wash my hair and dress. Eleven minutes. Back downstairs I start eating breakfast. Now it's 9:44. After I pour a coffee it's 9:52. Breakfast, unrushed, took eight minutes. I wash the dishes in four minutes flat.

I take the coffee upstairs to my study and turn on my computer. My computer requires a minute and a half just to load the desktop icons. I log on to my email account and read my new messages. This takes ten minutes, usually. If I have to respond immediately to an email, I'm there longer. I look up at the clock: it's 10:07. I finish my coffee and go to the bathroom to blow-dry my hair and brush my teeth. Five minutes there, now it's 10:12. If I had to leave now for an appointment, I'd go downstairs, gather my keys, wallet, cellphone and whatever else I needed and head out. That takes another four minutes. By 10:17 I'd be in the garage and putting my things in the car before opening up the garage door (it's manual), moving the car out of the garage and then reclosing the door. It would now be 10:21. A record. One phone call, a complicated email, and that departure time could easily be pushed to 10:41.

On a good morning I can begin work in my study at 11:00, and on an interrupted morning, by 11:45. On the days I'm not teaching I work for four hours in the afternoon—though, if I have any errands to do (grocery shopping, bookstore visits, research), I try to leave the house by 1:30 p.m. to get a few things done before rush hour, which starts at 3:00 p.m. and can add as much as an hour to any trip. "Take care of the minutes, for the hours will take care of themselves," Lord Chesterfield said. But the fact remains, given my morning routine, I really can only trim a few minutes off here and there.

I have a self-winding dress watch that I wear for formal occasions. It will run for a few days after I take it off, but it has almost always stopped by the time I put it on again. There is a little magnifying lens built into the crystal that enlarges the tiny date window. The date is usually a week or two behind. To advance it by a single day I have to pull out the crown and twirl the hour and minute hands through an entire twenty-four-hour cycle. If the watch is one or two weeks behind, twirling the crown is a laborious, finger-cramping exercise. But I don't find it tedious. I use it as a memory test. In my mind's eye I go through all those days and hours, visualizing what I was doing at 2:00 p.m., then 3:00, then 4:00 p.m. and so on, right through each day in succession.

Because of my familiarity with fast-forwarding DVDs, the exercise is not only easy, it's also kind of fun. I see myself rocketing out of bed, dashing around the house and leaping out the door and into my car. My drive to the university is more like the Grand Prix. I teach frantically, gesturing and pacing like someone on amphetamines, then zoom downtown to meet my hyper-animated friends for a frenzied restaurant dinner. After speeding home I sit fidgeting in front of the television for a few seconds, then race to the bathroom, run down the hall and bound into bed, lights out. I thrash around under the covers for a while, then the windows brighten and I'm up again to repeat the process.

DOING TIME

> We who live in prison, and in whose lives there is no event
> but sorrow, have to measure time by throbs of pain, and
> the record of bitter moments.
> —*Oscar Wilde*

Although most of us don't share Wilde's particular anguish, we are all prisoners of time, sentenced by the necessities of life and urban congestion. The difference is that we don't serve our sentences consecutively but in small portions. In a lifetime the average North American spends over nine months commuting, two years shopping and two more years cooking and washing up. Twenty-seven years are given over to sleeping, four years to eating, and twenty to working. Five months are spent talking on the phone, which pales beside the five and a half years spent watching television. Three long months are wasted waiting for someone. But it isn't all tedium. Given a fifty-five-year-long active sex life, the average person will spend four blissful months having sex.

One of the obvious ways of gaining more time, of slowing down the speed of the world around us, is to squeeze more time out of the hours we have. If you can do in five minutes something that takes others ten minutes, you prevail, you get there faster. Nowhere is that more apparent than in sports, particularly at the Olympic level. The difference between gold and silver can be measured in hundredths of a second, though at such infinitesimal increments it seems to me that our ability to measure small amounts of time has become an abstract, cruel taskmaster, extracting winners and losers from almost equal performances. All athletes excel at doing something fast, and their complex physical accomplishments are the result of a special kind of intelligence.

For sports, music and any activity that requires the co-ordination of hundreds of muscles, our brains have a clever assistant called the cerebellum. A knot of grey matter located at the back of the brain, the cerebellum is dedicated solely to storing the memories of complex movements. We train our cerebellum when, for instance, we learn to walk, ride a bicycle or play arpeggios on the piano. The cerebellum allows us to do things that call for lightning-fast reflexes, by re-enacting the exact sequences unconsciously. Playing an arpeggio on the piano, one of the most complex and quick of all human achievements, involves a series of finger motions well beyond the normal human reaction time of .02 seconds, but it's possible because all the fingering sequences are preloaded, as it were, in the cerebellum.

Yet our mind, the cortex, has no such accomplice. We may be able to train ourselves to think more quickly and clearly, but there are limits to what we can fit into a week. For most of us, just juggling our careers and lives is so complicated and demanding that if we can muddle through a day, no less a year, we feel as if we've accomplished something. To try to speed up my day, I recently consulted a free website on time management. It told me — not surprisingly — to prioritize. I should organize all my tasks into four categories: important and urgent, important and not urgent, not important but urgent, and not important and not urgent.

The key, the site suggested, was to learn to say no to tasks in the last two categories in order to free up more time for tasks in the first two. But I'm a master of deferral. It's like the old joke, "I've got a procrastination problem that, one day, I'm going to do something about." Pinned to my cork bulletin board in the kitchen is a list of household jobs that has been posted there for years. The top three are: repair the back fence, put silicone sealer in the gap between the baseboard and the floor in the front bedroom, and replace the screws on the French-door hinge in the living room. I suppose these fall under the "not important and not urgent" category, though if I ignore them long enough, they will become urgent. The time-management site understands this. According to it, the "not important" tasks have a "tendency to become emergencies if they are neglected." If you drive a car, you're probably familiar with that effect. There's never enough time to stop by a gas station and fill up, but if you don't, eventually you'll run out. The bottom line seems to be do it all—just do it all in order.

Okay, but what about the things that aren't so easy to schedule? The marriage that is on the rocks and doesn't know it, or the torrid affair that any day might erupt into a scandal. How do you fit the fallout from these catastrophes into your day-planner? The heart, it seems, will not be time-managed. And what about finding some time for yourself? Time to think, to contemplate. I once heard a poet say that for a writer the perfect ratio of contemplative time to work time is three to one: three hours of what, to the casual observer, would appear to be puttering around, going on walks, perusing the wares in second-hand stores or simply standing at windows and staring vacantly out, to one hour of sitting down at the computer and writing. This is because, he claimed, all writers need downtime for their unconscious minds to consolidate the complexities of their current work. That way, when they do sit down to write, the writing flows easily. "It takes a lot of time being a genius," Gertrude Stein once quipped. "You have to sit around so much doing nothing."

◆ ◆ ◆

But anyone can benefit from sitting around doing nothing. Because the world itself never stops. The wind blows, the sun shines. Today I sat out on my patio, doing nothing except sip a glass of shiraz and watch an empyrean late afternoon turn into evening. The sky was clear, the sweltering humidity of the last few days comfortably gone. The sunlight had a particular clarity, an emptiness, or maybe that was me, responding to the angle of sun, which is imperceptibly beginning to decline. Time didn't stop, it didn't even slow down, but my own tranquility and enjoyment of the moment created an intimate theatre of time. Sunset became a mixture of incremental changes and direct movement.

Far above me, a silvery jet skimmed across the sky. It was silent and tiny and left a straight white contrail that gradually transformed into an irregular line of puffy cumulus clouds. Looking west, I watched the pink edge of the setting sun disappear behind my neighbour's roof. The colour of the sunlight was changing constantly, though so gradually that I could never be sure when yellow turned to orange, and orange to pink. I looked up again at the jet contrail and there was hardly anything left—only a faint series of cloudlets. Above them, even higher, was a gauzy, rippled ocean of cirrus clouds, pale yet perfectly detailed.

A black squirrel ran across the lawn and climbed up the east fence, where it perched on the same post that the owl had perched on many months before. The yard was growing darker, more mysterious. When I looked up at the clouds again, everything had changed. All of them, the cirrus and the cumulus, had turned bright sulphur yellow as the sun began to touch the horizon. A flock of sparrows landed on the fence across the yard from the squirrel and sang up a storm. Were they gossiping, recounting their adventures from the day? The last sunlight, now a deep yellow-orange, caught the leaves in the treetops as the wind lifted up their silver undersides in languorous waves.

The clouds above the setting sun began to turn bright orange. The treetops that just moments ago had been alight were now eclipsed by a kind of aquatic shade. My present, I realized, was being sustained by the immediate past. Things remained the same, or changed so gradually that the present moment seemed to linger longer than it actually did. The clouds, the great oaks—everything around me seemed caught in a stuttering permanence.

Now the sunset started to transform into a spectacular conflagration. The whole western sky was domed with a filigree of fire as the cirrus clouds turned electric pink. It was an epic sunset, filled with burning galleons adrift on a light blue ocean. Ever the same and never the same from second to second in my absolute theatre of time. Each successive spreading ledge of flame surmounted the last in colour and intensity, like a Beethoven finale. Time was a conductor with time on her hands, touching each cloud, each leaf, each feather in turn, her masterpiece of nuance never ending. I had been embraced by time. And I had matched it, stride for stride, by simply opening myself to one of its spectacles.

Chapter Eight

THE CLOCK WITHIN

time *n.* 1. Duration, indefinitely continued existence,
progress of this viewed as affecting persons or things.
—*Oxford Concise Dictionary*

The light this first, misty morning of August was a powdery gold. It was as if everything—my yard, the neighbourhood, the city—had been enclosed in a giant greenhouse. The day lilies in the laneway were refulgent with copper blooms, and the heavy foliage of the butternut rising above my neighbour's yard was as still as sculpture. Everything was waiting; there was an electric, sensual anticipation in the atmosphere. This August reverie of mist and light and foliage has always reminded me of the paintings of the French artists Jean-Honoré Fragonard and William Bougereau. The same diffuse light illuminated their paintings of mythological nudes and cavorting gentry. Yet there is something of Correggio in the air, too. My garden could have been a backdrop to Correggio's painting of Jupiter and Io, where Jupiter, disguised as a cloud, embraces Io. She has turned her head to kiss the wilful vapour. All morning I've heard the low, distant rumble of thunder. Perhaps this afternoon my thirsty lawn will drink some rain.

Like July, August is named after a Roman emperor. But Augustus was more beloved by the ancient Romans than Julius Caesar; indeed,

Augustus was regarded as Rome's most benevolent ruler. His original name was Octavian, meaning "eighth," so it was the eighth month that was designated to honour him. Historians mark the Augustan age as the apogee of Roman civilization, mainly because the reign of Augustus oversaw an extraordinary rejuvenation of the infrastructure. He said that he found Rome a city of brick and left it a city of marble. The month of August finds summer a season of silver and leaves it a season of gold. I've always wondered why there is no North American holiday to celebrate August. In Canada we have a civic day off, marked by a long weekend during the first week of August, but nothing that acknowledges the month itself—the sun-bleached fields, the ripening peaches, the hazy afternoon vistas of distant forests and cities shimmering in the heat. At least Italy has a holiday that recognizes August. Celebrated on August 15 and called *ferragosto*, it's the descendant of the old Roman holiday of Feriae Augusti, declared by Augustus as a holiday and a time to honour the harvest gods. Most contemporary Italians observe it with a picnic banquet at their favourite country retreat. Then they go on holiday.

◆ ◆ ◆

This afternoon it didn't rain. The main event was the landing of a peregrine falcon on top of the old television antenna at the back of my neighbour's house. It was a female; I could tell by her large size and the dark barring across her breast, and she was not welcome. Local birds use the metal rods of the antenna as a perch and song roost. The multilingual starlings gurgle, purr and click from there, the grackles and sparrows land on it to survey adjacent yards for tidbits, mourning doves coo poignantly from its pulpit and, in the late afternoon, robins and cardinals turn it into a concert platform for their elaborate territorial performances. But today it was the peregrine's turn to rule the roost, and the other birds, knowing her to be a killer, were furious. They dove angrily at her and made close, twittering flybys. A pair of starlings even sat on the far side of the same antenna rung and screeched at the deadly intruder. The peregrine was unruffled. She made a few urgent, piercing calls and then launched herself off the antenna. She was looking for something.

An hour later a fledgling peregrine, almost full-grown, landed on the same antenna. I decided that it must have left the nest on its first solo flight and become separated from its mother, who would have been keeping close watch. I wondered where she'd got to. And I wondered what the Roman augurs would have made of my peregrine sightings. In terms of omens, eagles and falcons are thought to represent royalty. I'd like to think that the spirit of Augustus was conferring a benediction on me in recognition of my loyalty to his month.

◂ ◂ ◂

In terms of the distance covered by earth during its orbit around the sun, August is about fifty million miles long, which means that since I saw the owl in March, the earth has travelled over two hundred million miles along its orbit. Time *is* space. And yet I don't have any sense of so much distance, except that in August the light begins to slant, and by the end of the month there's a bit of a *fin de siècle* nostalgia to its imperceptible limpidness. But still, August is invincible summer, the summer having reigned for months by the time August begins. Every living thing has settled into an aestive pattern that seems endless, as if it had always been thus. The paths that thread the fields and forests are well packed and dry, the corn is tasselling, and every backyard swimming pool is a jewelled fragment of Caribbean diaspora. You can let yourself imagine that summer will never end.

But the clock is ticking, and it makes for a slight undertone of urgency, especially towards the end of August. The backyard dinner parties get more exuberant at night, the vacationing children become a little more wanton. Still, much as we may try to hold on to summer, the calendar flips ahead. The sun sets just a little earlier every week, and while we linger in the pink-gold light of August evenings, our inner clocks are being reset.

INTERNAL CLOCKS AND MEMORY

> We live in deeds, not years; in thoughts, not breaths;
> In feelings, not in figures on a dial.
> We should count time by heart-throbs.
> —*Philip James Bailey*

Several layers of time coexist within us, like nested Russian dolls. In our deepest, most physical existence, we have body time, based on the circadian rhythms of our internal organs and hormones. These rhythms tell us when to sleep and when to wake up. They flow in tides of subtle moods and changing awareness. Our body time influences our mental or clock time, but ultimately our minds are independent of our bodies. The abstractions of past and future that allow us to plan our lives according to experience are the central index of our conscious lives and represent the outermost layer of personal time. But beneath our conscious, and unconscious, experience, we also possess deep brain time, the embedded clock that has us waking up seconds before the morning alarm rings. Neurologists theorize that this clock is located somewhere in the ventral striatum, and that its rate depends on the steady release of dopamine in the brain. The time distortion caused by marijuana, among other mind-altering drugs, is likely due to its effects on the dopaminergic system.

A Philadelphia psychologist named Stuart Albert recently proved that subjective, conscious time awareness, and possibly deep brain time, could be tinkered with. He shut two groups of volunteers into two separate rooms over a period of several days. Unbeknownst to the volunteers, he had modified the wall clocks. In one room, the clock ran at half speed; in the other, at double speed. Not only did the volunteers turn out to be unaware of the temporal sleight-of-hand, but Albert also discovered that their mental functions automatically adjusted to the two different paces. In memory tests, the average rate of forgetting, usually regarded as a brain function independent of the clock, was faster in the speedy group. And likewise, when asked to estimate various durations, the answers corresponded to each group's relative time frame. It would be interesting to see what would happen if the experiment were to run longer. Would the volunteers' circadian clocks eventually rebel? And what would happen if the subjective abstraction of clock time was removed altogether? The answer lies beneath the ground.

In January 1989, a young Italian volunteer named Stefania Follini began a solo four-month deep-cave sojourn to determine how our internal sense of time is affected if there are no clocks and no alternations of day and night. Stefania ate, slept and worked in a windowless twelve-by-twenty-foot room built within a cave in New Mexico. Within weeks her days had lengthened to twenty-five hours, and by the end of her sojourn she was staying awake up to forty hours at a time and sleeping between fourteen and twenty-two hours. After being in the cave for over four months, and just before the researchers told her that it was May and time to end the experiment, she was asked to estimate how much time had passed. "Two months," she guessed. Her internal clock had reset its own rhythm to a tempo much slower than everyone else's. It seems that without constant resetting by the alternation of night and day, our internal clocks drift, and hers had drifted wildly. The final result, for her, was equivalent to time travel. She was transported two months into the future. No wonder her first words—when, sun-dazzled, she faced the reporters and waved to the waiting crowd—were, "Wow, man."

Time and Memory

Before technology turned us into creatures of time, we, like every other living being on this planet, had our hands too full of the demands of the present to notice the narrative, linear universe around us. We lived instead in circular time. Even though the stone-age world flowed irrevocably into the future—we got older, our tools wore down and new ones had to be made—time was more seasonal than sequential. The fruits we ate ripened on the same bushes at the same time of year in the same location, we knew where and when migratory animals had shown up previously, and so it paid off to have a good long-term memory to predict the future based on the past. With the advent of language, these lasting memories began to be shared with others, and the roots of civilization began. It is our special privilege as human beings to have more memory than we need. We are blessed with extraordinary, almost supernatural memory, memories that reanimate the past, and now, through our media, are also able to virtually reconstitute it. We realize the past more fully than any other living thing. It is so alive to us that it is almost as if our purpose here on earth is to make history conscious of itself—to incarnate our past, our species and our planet in living memory.

In our waking lives, our long-term memories are central to our identity. I am defined by a very specific set of personal, intimate memories. I remember a sunny winter afternoon when I was three and my older brother let me ride on his shoulders. I remember my first palm tree. It was in the south of France and I was nineteen. I can feel my brother's shoulders again, hear the crunch of the snow, see every frond of that palm tree. No one else can lay claim to these cardinal memories, this particular string of events that formed who I am. Memories are precise landmarks in the ocean of time; more than anything else, they represent us to ourselves. In fact, it's not overstating the case to say that we *are* our memories, and that without them we would be empty. Perhaps that is why, when people are on the threshold of life and death, their whole life passes before their eyes. And why we find the stories of amnesiacs so compelling. Without memories amnesiacs are like babies, like clones, bereft of identity.

◂ ◂ ◂

Once, when I was sleeping in a cabin in northern Ontario, I had a dream about cardinal memories. In the dream I walked through an abandoned city in some sort of post-apocalyptic world overgrown with vegetation. I came upon a concrete foundation that had a stairwell descending into its depths. I went down and there was a large concrete room, like an art gallery, illuminated by a few holes in the ceiling. Along the walls of the room were glass cases holding museum-style dioramas. I went up to the dioramas and looked at each one in turn. They were all three-dimensional, very lifelike depictions of human figures caught in the midst of life. Perhaps modelled in wax, I couldn't tell. One scene in particular stood out for me: it was of a husband embracing his wife, two small children at their feet, both of whom were embracing his legs. The group was standing on a lawn not far from a dark blue, old-model sedan. Behind them the walls of the diorama depicted a small-town airport in the mid-1950s, with its control tower and terminal, all beneath a blue summer sky. I could see that a light breeze caught the wife's hair, and I knew that this reunion must have been the happiest moment of the husband's life.

Each subsequent case also showed a person's happiest moment, and I walked, spellbound, down the whole row. I remember water dripped from the crumbling ceiling and occasionally fell onto my head. After a while the tableaux, though still joyful, took on an almost funereal air. Where were these people now? I wondered. Had they chosen their happiest moments or had the moments been determined by some higher force? I woke up and considered the dream. I thought that I must have been realizing how, in our long-term memories, certain moments—happy or sad, traumatic or wistful—stand still, frozen in time, and how, altogether, they reinforce that which feels changeless within us. We are the same person now as we were years ago—a little older, certainly, but the same. And it is this unchanging self that is timeless. Our pure existence is profoundly felt as an eternal present, as if the passage of time were the illusion. Although we only really exist in the present, all of the experience that forms our identity comes from the past, which is why time and memory have such an intimate relationship. We can't be who we are unless we *remember* who we were. Long-term memory is the trail we leave behind us, the crumbs that lead us back to ourselves. It is a bulwark against time's ceaseless forward momentum and thereby gives us a direct sense of the permanence of history.

◂ ◂ ◂

Short-term memory is something else entirely. It exists almost completely within the present and only retrieves the recent past. We use it as a practical tool to help us remember that a computer is on, that a casserole is in the oven or that a friend is coming by to pick up a jacket he left behind. Short-term memories are dispensable temporal maps. They are like a dissolving trace that evaporates as we move through our lives. When we walk through a new building and notice the colour of the walls, the arrangement of the courtyard, the corridors and windows, these stay fresh in our minds for hours afterwards. But if we don't revisit the building for few days, our short-term memories of it begin to fade. It's as though, in our absence, things gradually disappear. If the building itself started to disintegrate as quickly as our short-term memory of it disappeared, it would be rubble within a few days, if not hours.

That is true of the majority of short-term memories—unless they are cardinal, incidental events don't persist in our mind. But some of them do. Out of our torrent of experience there are also strangely persistent memories of certain things, memories that should be dispensable but for some reason linger on and turn into long-term traces similar to cardinal memories, unaffected by the passage of time. I remember the exact layout and colours of an outdoor patio where I had dinner once in Miami. I can almost hear the wind in the palms above the tables, the sounds of a jet overhead, even the colour of the straw in my drink—as if I'd made a video recording of an unexceptional twenty-minute period in my life.

But memory more often transforms, and if it is our most intimate link to the changeless aspect of time that is the past, it is often a fragile one. Aside from family movies and photographs, we have no dioramas to revisit. Through the ever-changing window of our minds, the past can become fluid, elusive, especially when we dream. If memory and consciousness are yoked to time's arrow, no part of us is so independent of that arrow as our unconscious minds. The unconscious seems timeless sometimes—in dreams we talk to friends and relatives who have died, or we are suddenly children, living at home with our parents again. As a result dream time is discontinuous and strange. Dreams play with time. That could be why some of them seem so elusive upon awakening—maybe their "fleeting" quality is the collision of conscious time and unconscious time.

The atemporal world of the unconscious alters the time-bound expectations of our waking lives, submerging us in a paradoxical world of simultaneous narratives, of backwards stories and jumps through seasons and years. I think of dreams as the working edge of an encounter between the version of ourselves that we have built up from long-term memories and the timelessness of the unconscious. In retrospect my diorama dream seems to be a message from my unconscious about just that nexus. At our centre we are eternal beings that slough off the years, impervious to time's arrow. Neuroscience appears to support the atemporal nature of our brains. Magnetic resonance images of volunteers asked to think of the future, and then of the past, revealed that both future and past were processed in the same parts of the brain. In dreams memories become alive—they are no longer *images* of the past, we *live* them. Our sleeping minds are illuminated by the timeless radiance of the unconscious.

The Art of Time

"Time and I against any two," Cardinal Mazarin once declared during the reign of Louis XIV. He was quoting an old Spanish proverb, but he was referring to the treacherous realm of French court intrigue in the seventeenth century. Indeed, given enough time, anything can be done: pyramids can be built, empires established and books written. Though we don't have all the time in the world. "*Vita brevis est, ars longa*"—"Life is short, the art long," as Hippocrates wrote in the fourth century B.C.

Time-based arts, those that depend on time itself as an essential part of their realization, have always been the most popular. Film, dance, music and theatre could not exist independently of time the way that sculpture, architecture and painting do. I suspect that the reason we prefer time-based art forms is that they are so much more like us: they live and move. The non-time-based arts have a less immediate, more eternal attraction. Writing, I think, occupies a position midway between the moving and stationary arts, because even though letters are immobile, we animate them with imagination.

The written arts have a considerable advantage over improvised ones, such as jazz or improvised theatre, and somewhat of an advantage over painting or sculpture, in that the writer can take the time to get it right. With time on her side, a novelist can labour for years on a single book, considering every angle of plot, tone and structure. There are no muddy areas of overpainting, no seams in chiselled marble that reveal where a limb once broke off. What the writer sacrifices for this perfection, however, are the sensual pleasures of paint, of fragrant pigments and swirls of form, the gesture and movement. The writer's medium is punishingly minimal; emotion, time and love are reduced to a series of tiny, insect-like silhouettes on paper. And there's none of the freedom of dance, the exultation of music, the physical mastery of a beautiful instrument. There's no clay or stone or towering pediments or sound and fury, and, except for the finished book, there's nothing you can point to and say, "Look." It is a solitary profession. The writer works alone and the reader reads alone. Both share the isolation of page or screen, the silence of inner codes.

While writers have the luxury of taking their time, the amount of time that goes into perfecting any work of art is invisible to the audience, who apprehend the years of toil in one whole, or continuous, experience, as if the work appeared *ex nihilo*. The time spent on composition is hidden, like the underwater section of an iceberg. But I think that audiences sense the time anyway, and it charges the work with a special energy. The compressed potential of all those hours of labour is released during the performance of the music, during the reading of the novel, and upon viewing a statue or great building. The experience becomes a secular way of touching the divine, the more than human.

◂　◂　◂

This afternoon, while I was listening to Glenn Gould playing Bach's *Goldberg Variations*, I realized that during the past century the performance of music has begun to take on some of the characteristics of writing. Before the advent of electronic recordings, music performances were liable to spontaneous irregularities—a cellist might cough, or a violin string might snap—marring an otherwise perfect performance. But now a musician can insist on take after take, as Glenn Gould did so famously when he was recording the *Variations*. In the film *Glenn Gould Hereafter*, a documentary by Bruno Monsaingeon, Gould talks about the manipulation of time.

> You know, this is a very cloistered environment, this world
> of the recording studio. It is, quite literally, an environment
> where time turns in upon itself, where, as in a cloister, one
> is able to withstand the frantic pursuit of the transient, the
> moment-to-moment, day-by-day succession of events . . .
> the first take may well be preceded by the sixteenth, and
> both may be linked by inserts recorded years apart. It is
> an environment where the magnetic compulsion of time
> is suspended, though warped, or at least it is a vacuum in
> a sense, a place where one can properly feel that the most
> horrendously constricting force of nature—the inexorable
> linearity of time—has, to a remarkable extent, been
> circumvented.

There was something in the music of the *Goldberg Variations*, as performed so precisely by Glenn Gould, that evoked the sunlight coming through the window. I could sense both the time that Bach put into the composing and the hours that Gould invested in practising, listening and re-recording. Yet the music floated out of my speakers as fresh and crystalline as if it were being downloaded from heaven. The inaudible substrata of time within time had polished the notes like diamonds.

BACKWARDS TIME

My banana tree is taking off like Jack's beanstalk. Almost every week it sprouts a big new leaf, always larger than the last. I measured the newest one: thirty-one inches long and thirteen inches wide. The next leaf—starting to unfurl now in a luscious, pale green funnel—will be even bigger. My neighbors are impressed. But I worry that with August almost over, the nights will soon be getting cooler, and longer, and the banana tree will suffer.

My potted fan palm also did well this summer. To keep track of how fast it's growing, I scratch the month and year each leaf emerges in small letters at the top the leaf's stem, and this year it produced a giant fan every month, a real vegetative factory. The August leaf, still expanding, is thirty-one inches wide by twenty-five inches long, not including the stem. But, like the banana tree, the palm is at risk. It's not scheduled to be picked up and shipped off to the greenhouse for overwintering until the middle of October, and even though the transition into autumn is an incremental process, something that plants can adapt to easily within their special time frame, September seems to be creeping up on me faster than I expected. The seasons bleed into each other.

◂ ◂ ◂

The rhythms of our days, the cycle of the seasons, turn time into an ourobors—the hooped snake that eats its own tail. Each day, every season slides incrementally into the next, greased by routine and familiarity. In W. B. Yeats' mystic book *A Vision*, much of which was dictated to him by his wife while she was supposedly in contact with spirits, time is likened to two widening, interpenetrating spirals or cones (not unlike an hourglass, though Yeats himself doesn't make the comparison). Time, for him, spiralled outwards into history, away from the present. Yet the fact that another cone, facing the opposite direction, was mirroring the first, meant that the past could return. What goes around comes around. The cones, or "gyres," as Yeats called them, were to his mind also representative of beauty and truth, the particular and the universal, value and fact, and quality and quantity. In his famous poem "The Second Coming," he interprets the gyres: "Turning and turning in the widening gyre / The falconer cannot hear the falcon;/ Things fall apart; the centre cannot hold; / Mere anarchy is loosed upon the world."

It's fascinating that Yeats came up with his vision of a cone to describe cosmic time only a few years after Einstein used light cones as a description of space-time. Circles within circles, spirals within cones and interpenetrating cones seemed to be in the air at the beginning of the twentieth century. But other minds had earlier pondered the cyclical nature of time. In 1882 Friedrich Nietzsche had published a book of lyric philosophy called *The Gay Science*, in which he spelled out his doctrine of the eternal return by means of an allegory called the Greatest Weight.

> What if, some day or night a demon were to steal after
> you into your loneliest loneliness and say to you: "This life
> as you now live it and have lived it, you will have to live

once more and innumerable times more; and there will
be nothing new in it, but every pain and every joy and
every thought and sigh and everything unutterably small
or great in your life will have to return to you, all in the
same succession and sequence—even this spider and this
moonlight between the trees, and even this moment and I
myself. The eternal hourglass of existence is turned upside
down again and again, and you with it, speck of dust!"

Here is Yeats' cyclic time with a vengeance.

Nietzsche then goes on to explain how this idea, the weight of eternal repetition, could be used as a spiritual discipline to free the soul:

Would you not throw yourself down and gnash your teeth
and curse the demon who spoke thus? Or have you once
experienced a tremendous moment when you would have
answered him: "You are a god and never have I heard
anything more divine." If this thought gained possession
of you, it would change you as you are or perhaps crush
you. The question in each and every thing, "Do you desire
this once more and innumerable times more?" would lie
upon your actions as the greatest weight. Or how well
disposed would you have to become to yourself and to life
to crave nothing more fervently than this ultimate eternal
confirmation and seal?

Nietzsche's vision of the eternal return came to him while he was
walking through the woods beside Lake Silvaplana, not far from Surlei,
in the Alps, during August 1881. The eighth month proved a charm for
Friedrich. More of an idea or a Zen koan than an attempt to explain

reality the way Yeats did in *A Vision*, the eternal return nevertheless gives us hope of a future, however unchanging, whereas in Yeats' version, things incrementally fall apart. The circle is broken. Though sometimes we don't notice.

◂ ◂ ◂

Incremental phenomena are notoriously invisible. The house paint that fades over the years, the men who gradually lose their hair. What happens with the men is that one morning they notice a small, bare area and comb a few loose hairs over it. As the baldness spreads, they end up combing long strands from the sides of their heads right over their crowns. They didn't start out like that; they didn't wake up one morning and resolve to hide their bald domes with specially grown long strands of hair. It was an incremental process. Gaining weight is the same thing. People reach three hundred pounds gradually, deceiving themselves in the mirror like anti-anorexics.

If only we could reverse time, if only we could become young again, slimmer, with a full head of lustrous hair. But time's arrow cruelly points one way. With a few exceptions. In cyclotrons—"atom smashers," as they are otherwise known—physicists have discovered that the paths of certain quantum particles can only be explained if they have travelled backwards in time for a very brief period. And at the other scale of matter—the universe itself—there may be another temporal surprise in store.

One of the immutable cornerstones of physics is a principle called "reversibility," which states that every basic physical action in the universe could be reversed in time with no contradiction of the laws of nature—planets could circle the sun in reverse, atoms could spin in reverse, everything could go backwards and nothing would change. For this reason scientists think that time's arrow has no quantifiable direction—time is directionless. But hold on, you say. If people walked backwards and rain fell up into the sky, you would certainly notice a difference. Do physicists exist in the same world as us? *Time's Arrow*, a novel by Martin Amis, takes on this principle, depicting an impossible, disorienting world of people taking food out of their mouths and putting it on plates, feeding their money into bank machines. What Amis is wryly saying is that it is only common sense that time flows from the past into the future. But common sense often fails scientific rigour. After all, it seemed common sense that a heavy object would fall faster than a small one, or that the sun and planets would orbit the earth. But, surrounded as they are by daily, hourly evidence of time's arrow, scientists have found no irrefutable evidence to support time's flow in a single direction. Except, perhaps, for one renegade.

In the 1960s an astrophysicist named Thomas Gold proposed that time's arrow *was* pointed in one direction by the law of thermodynamics; the flow of heat away from stars and into space. As the process cannot be reversed, as light and heat cannot flow backwards into the sun, it transcends the principle of reversibility. He reasoned further that not only is time's arrow directed by this process, but that time also relies on the expansion of the universe to keep soaking up the heat released by stars. Here's where things get interesting. If, at some point in the future, the universe should stop expanding (and many cosmologists believe it will), if the expansion of the universe eventually succumbs to the inevitable force of gravity, then radiation will start to converge instead of dissipating. At which point, Gold suggested, time will begin to run backwards and everything that has ever happened will happen again, only in reverse. Martin Amis may have been more prescient than he thought. Glenn Gould, Augustus, Correggio, W. B. Yeats and Nietzsche may, one day, walk this earth again.

◂ THE PAST ▸

Chapter Nine

Deep Time

> Deeper and deeper into Time's endless tunnel, does the
> winged soul, like a night-hawk, wend her wild way; and
> finds eternities before and behind; and her last limit is her
> everlasting beginning.
> —*Herman Melville*

The past is always giving us something new. The citizens of eighteenth-
century England never suspected that a lost world was buried in the
rock beneath their feet, but the nineteenth century brought the discovery of dinosaur bones—skeletons of fantastic creatures that had
lain unseen in the limestone for millions of years. The fossils revealed
an extraordinary world, very unlike Victorian England, inhabited by
giant lizards. A little later in the nineteenth century, archeologists
unearthed Egyptian tombs filled with the lavish spoils of an exotic
civilization. The most celebrated discovery of this kind was Howard
Carter's unearthing of the tomb of Tutankhamen in 1923. All at once
the ancient king's crypt was a time portal into the world. Pictures
of the ornate sarcophagus were relayed across the planet, and global interest spawned a whole economy devoted to the reproduction
of Egyptian figurines, jewellery, hairstyles, clothing and architecture.
And history continues to yield new cultures as well as extraordinary

animals completely new to science: the velociraptor that went on to star in *Jurassic Park*, the giant pterosaurs of the Cretaceous, with twenty-five-foot wingspans. Over the last two centuries, archeology and paleontology have brought us Herculaneum, mammoths, Troy, sabre-toothed tigers and Babylon.

◂ ◂ ◂

In a sense I've lived my whole life enmeshed in deep time. As a child I used to spend rainy Saturday afternoons leafing through picture books about prehistoric eras. I was enthralled by the lush illustrations of the world of dinosaurs and the tropical Eden they inhabited. In that sense I was like many other young boys who develop a fascination with dinosaurs, though perhaps I took it a little further. My friends and I used to play at being dinosaurs in backyards. I relished the role of *Tyrannosaurus rex*, king of the dinosaurs, most fearsome of the Cretaceous predators. I think I was pretty good at it. I'd curl up my arms on my chest and stick out two hooked fingers to simulate the strangely diminutive front legs of the Tyrannosaurus. Then, assuming a slight crouching position, I'd mimic snapping huge jaws filled with razor-sharp teeth as I roared and chased my friends, whom I'd assigned to be harmless herbivores.

My father, an avid geologist and physiographer, fuelled my interest not only in the Cretaceous period, but in all prehistoric eras. From as far back as I can remember, he was constantly describing the origins of the landforms around our home. His extemporized lectures were especially entertaining when we went on intercity car trips, which became journeys through time as well as space. Under his spell, landscapes melted away as cataclysms erupted out of the hills and valleys. That mound over there was a moraine, a ridge of boulders and gravel deposited by a glacier thirty thousand years ago. That limestone mesa eroded into its shape gradually, over thousands of years. Niagara Falls was once close to the southern shore of Lake Ontario. Over the millennia it worked its way up the Niagara River to its present location, halfway between Lake Ontario and Lake Erie. The limestone cliffs beside the access ramp were deposited millions of years ago at the bottom of a shallow tropical ocean. Through his eyes the landscape became a time machine.

He told me that the limestone boulders in the rock garden at the back of our lawn were made of ocean deposits laid down millions of years before dinosaurs existed. That meant that the fossil shells that studded the rocks were from a time even more primeval and strange than that in which the dinosaurs existed. It was a time called the Devonian period, when there were no land animals at all, and only a very few primitive plants grew at the edges of the oceans.

Looking at those fossil shells I could almost see their colours. I would go into a kind of trance, the rock would disappear and I'd envision the shadows of trilobites and armoured fish flickering across the sandy bottom of a warm tropical lagoon on a sunny afternoon untold years ago. (My reveries of primeval reefs eventually grew into a love of snorkelling in modern reefs. After all, coral reefs haven't changed that much over four hundred million years, although, of course, the design of the fish has been updated.)

I became completely fascinated with the Devonian period and borrowed book after book from our little local library, often reborrowing the same book so that I could linger over the illustrations of the unlikely-looking creatures that teemed in those ancient tropical oceans. Gardens of crinoids that looked like tulips made out of beads waved in the currents between the coral reefs, their feathery calcium petals filtering plankton out of the water. Swimming around the coral and crinoids were trilobites. I loved their compact, sculptural bodies and the fact that they were divided into three segments, like insects. I imagined that they were as colourful as reef fish are today. The first true fishes were also alive in the Devonian, although most of them were protected by plated armour. For good reason.

Some of the things that have emerged from prehistory are not as attractive as others. Velociraptors are fearsome, as are the tryannosaurs. But not all dangerous fauna were land-based. When I was a child leafing through illustrated books on prehistoric water creatures, I used to avoid the pages with illustrations of eurypterids, otherwise known as sea scorpions. It was an instinctive reaction of mine. Eurypterids were nasty customers indeed. They looked like a cross between a scorpion and a lobster, with two large paddle arms at the front end and a long, poisonous stinger at the rear. Some specimens were nine feet long, which makes them the biggest arthropods ever. Not only were they the top predator of their era, they were also real survivors. Their original colour, deep amber brown, is as bright today (when chipped out of rock by fossil hunters) as it was in the Devonian period. In certain cases, their tough, leathery shells resisted the mineralizing effects of fossilization, so that some specimens, though locked in limestone for four hundred million years, are still flexible today. Talk about a time capsule.

As the Devonian period waned into the Carboniferous period, several species of eurypterids evolved to inhabit fresh water while others probably became land-dwelling. It could be that scorpions are their diminutive descendants. And if giant eurypterids had not died out, they might be as ubiquitous now as their Carboniferous brethren, the cockroaches. Land-dwelling eurypterids would make living in the tropics impossible. To me, even our two-hundred-million-year distance seems uncomfortably close.

Because fossils were the most direct way of experiencing the Devonian period, I spent a lot of time at the the Royal Ontario

Museum in Toronto, where my father was an associate archeologist. While he met with fellow archeologists he would turn me loose, and I'd head straight for my devotional temple—the invertebrate paleontology gallery. I passed many afternoons there, poring over glass display cases that contained row after row of impossibly perfect fossils: slate slabs scattered with dozens of glistening black trilobites that looked as if they might swim away at any moment; groves of crinoids that seemed to have turned to stone as they undulated in the warm sea. Many of the fossils appeared to have been carved out of stone by meticulous sculptors. There were also cases full of ornate shells, sometimes completely freed from the rock, as marvellous as any that adorn the remote beaches of today's Pacific Ocean.

My supreme thrill came when my family went on picnic excursions to Rock Glen, a small limestone gorge in the countryside near my hometown in southwestern Ontario. This was pure time travel. We would eat our sandwiches at the top of the glen overlooking the waterfall, then explore the forested gorge. The shale and limestone there brimmed with fossils, and because the rock was so soft, the fossils tumbled out whole and rolled down the sides of the gorge, where they collected in drifts by the side of the river. It was fossil heaven, where the border between the present and prehistory blurred. On the upper slopes I could coax soft layers of slate apart with my hands, like leaves in the book of time. And in the shallow water of the stream at the bottom of the gorge, the submerged fossils of trilobites looked as though they might be grazing on the algae there.

It sometimes seemed to me that I was trapped in a relatively uninteresting epoch that was not natural to my inclinations, that I was not of my time. I was a citizen, and still am, of deep time. Periods spanning millions of years strike me as natural, though I must admit, when *billions* are mentioned, things get a little abstract, even for me. I think that the origin of my familiarity with deep time came from a revelation I had one rainy, cold Sunday afternoon in late November, when I was eleven.

I was leafing through a copy of *The World We Live In*, a big, wonderfully illustrated hardcover book about the history of life on earth. The page that caught my eye that afternoon, even though I'd looked at it many times before, was an illustration of the glacial age. It showed a four-thousand-foot wall of ice at the advancing edge of a continental glacier. You could see the lines and crevices along the top of the glacier, which stretched back in the distance to a grey polar darkness. There was an apocalyptic, icy grandeur to the scene.

As I stared dreamily at the illustration of the lake at the base of the glacier—at the small icebergs floating in the water and the evergreen forest growing bravely beside the glacier itself—a shock of pure, deep time went through me. I knew that the location of that picture could easily have been right where our house now stood, these hundreds of millennia later. It was as if something within me had done the math. I could actually feel what existing for ten thousand years would be like, and I was filled with both dread and awe. It wasn't just a sense of mortality, of how short life is in comparison to these millennial spans; it was the direct sensation within my body of every echoing century. I stood on that chilly shore.

That experience changed me, and though I have never really, physically grasped such a period of time since, the vision gave me a kind of fluency with time, one that allows me to directly sense the hoary patina of history that gilds all ancient artifacts. I still marvel at fossils, and I feel every bit as much excitement going into a museum today as I did as a child. Also, limestone continues to hold dreams and nostalgia for me, vistas of lost epochs and spectacular new fossils. Limestone is sheer potential. Who knows what wonders are hidden within it, what secrets it might yield of time past?

LIMESTONE AND CLAY

Limestone isn't simply a chronological record of prehistory, it is compressed time. The horizontal layers you see in road cuts through limestone beside highways were laid down millions of years ago as sediment at the bottom of oceans. I once calculated how much time was contained in a vertical inch of limestone, at least as it is represented by the dolomite cliff that Niagara Falls pours over. I divided the height of the cliff, 167 feet, by the number of years it represented, about thirty million, and came up with 15,000 years an inch. If you consider that the first city-states arose in Mesopotamia only 10,500 years ago, then the staggering age of this rock starts to become apparent. The layers of sedimentary stone that form the walls of the Grand Canyon in Colorado are even more impressive; they contain a continuous vertical record of 330 million years of life on earth. When you stand on the lip of the Grand Canyon, you are looking into an abyss of time as well as space.

On top of holding the often perfectly cast remains of extinct creatures, of shells and dinosaurs, limestone also preserves single days—indeed, single moments. The trackway of a small, birdlike dinosaur discovered recently in Alberta is a record of a few seconds in time millions of years ago, when the dinosaur foraged at the muddy edge of a river.

There are other fossil records of this same kind of ephemeral, transitory moment. A few decades ago, in an area of northern Tanzania called Laetoli, the trackways of two, possibly three, hominids were discovered preserved in stone. The tracks were so clear that they looked as if they had just been made the day before; in fact, they have since been calculated to be over 3.5 million years old. The actions of this small group of pre-humans, walking through the freshly fallen ash near an active volcano after a light rainfall, have been reconstructed, and so we know that at one point the footprints stop, indicating that the group paused to look around them. Did the nearby volcano erupt briefly? Did a carnivore roar? And where were they going? If there were two of them, it appears it was a male and a female. But if there were three—and most anthropologists believe there were—why did the second, smaller male not only walk behind the first two, but also deliberately step in the tracks of the first male?

Trackways are not the only record of transitory events. One of my favourite kinds of preserved moments in time are fossil ripple marks. More than representing a particular few minutes in time or revealing the behaviour of a creature, they represent a day, perhaps a single afternoon, in a shallow coral reef lagoon. Ripple patterns in underwater sand change gradually, from one day to the next, as the waves above transform them. In the Caribbean I've snorkelled over acres of flat white lagoon sand, scanning the smoothly corrugated contours for brittle stars and sand divers. I've always found this expanse of sinuous texture, like a giant's fingerprint, to be meditative and idyllic. White underwater sand, lit turquoise by sea and sunlight, seems to me to be one of the essences of a tropical afternoon. But to come upon an identically contoured series of ripple marks, preserved in sandstone more than three hundred million years old, is to be sent back in time to an eerily similar lagoon lit by a similar sun. The earth was spinning more quickly then, so the primeval afternoon would end sooner than our afternoon does now, but the sand flats would be identical—until you reached the reef, that is. Then there would be some surprises in store: schools of squids housed in coiled shells, foraging trilobites and fish whose heads were covered with bony plates.

TIME PORTAL: THE SANGAMONIAN BRICK WORKS

It's already September. The summer flew by, though early September is, for me, the pinnacle of August. The weather is hot and clear, the cicadas are singing, and my yard is at its lushest. The banana tree has six big leaves, and my palm has a new leaf beginning to fan open. This evening, when the sun was just beginning to throw the south side of my house into shade, there was a moment when every little bump and crevice on the bricks was cast into relief. In a brick just above and to the right of the back door, I noticed something that looked like a pawprint, and I stood up and took a closer look. It *was* a cat's footprint—judging from its size, a kitten's. "How's that possible?" I thought. Then it struck me. Many years ago that brick, along with other wet bricks, must have lain on an outdoor rack before being fired in a kiln. That's when a kitten walked across them. I began to search for more pawprints and I found some, probably from the same kitten, on several bricks in my house. I found one on a brick in the alleyway between my neighbour's house and my own, and two others on the front of my house. I fantasized about removing the bricks and reconstructing the kitten's path, like a dinosaur trackway in a museum display. But they're fine where they are.

Long before I saw the kitten prints, I'd noticed other impressions in the brick: four indentations in a row that look like they were made by the tips of someone's fingers, and something that resembles the imprint of the side of a hand. Also, many of the bricks have ridges, possibly from spaces between the boards in the drying racks. All these indelible imprints, like footprints in wet concrete, are a permanent record of transient events—a kitten walking over damp clay on a warm spring evening, a worker testing the firmness of the bricks before he slides them into the red-hot kiln.

I did some research on the history of my house and discovered that it was built in 1913 and that the bricks used to construct its walls were supplied by the Don Valley Brick Works, located in a ravine in the city's southeast. At that time the bricks came in two colours, red and yellow. The yellow bricks were made of the clay quarried at the site, while the red bricks were made from limestone found beneath the clay. Because my house was built in 1913, I presume that my bricks were fired the year before, at least. They are a lovely hue of red, a warm, Pompeian terracotta. But my relationship with the brick works goes even deeper.

As I went through the history of the brick works, which began producing bricks in the late nineteenth century, I discovered the site included a unique prehistoric deposit from an interglacial era called the Sangamonian. I was hooked. The Don Valley Brick Works turned out to be the only place in Ontario with 120,000-year-old fossils from the Illinoian glacial period. Even more importantly, a very remarkable layer, the Don Formation, consisting of clay from the Sangamonian interglacial period, overlaid the Illinoian deposits. The name was exotic, lovely. It rolled seductively in my mouth. But it was the Sangamonian climate that I really liked. At the height of the Sangamonian, 115,000 years ago, Toronto was much warmer than it is today. Osage orange trees, pawpaws and wild rhododendrons adorned the slopes beside rivers where beavers the size of black bears swam. Semitropical insects got stuck in the clay, and sabre-toothed tigers prowled the thickets.

I decided to visit the fabled brickyards and see if I could find any Sangamonian fossils. The brick factory has closed down, but the city recently turned the buildings into a historical site and created a large park with ponds and walkways where the quarries were located. The works themselves are set in a large bowl formed by tall clay cliffs on two sides. Towards the west side are a few ponds where the old limestone quarry was located, and behind it is the famous north slope of the clay quarry. I clambered up the slope and spent the next half-hour splitting dry pieces of clay apart, looking for fossils. I didn't find a thing. I went to the western edge of the property, where Mud Creek cascades in a small waterfall, and walked along an embankment strewn with discarded limestone pieces. Here I was happily surprised.

The rocks were full of fossils: shells, feather stars, trilobites and coral. Some pieces even had ripple marks. During the Ordovician period—the time the limestone was formed—Toronto was on the equator (due to continental drift) and land plants hadn't evolved. It was late evening when I stumbled upon this treasure, and the sun was almost setting. It was a perfect summer evening and it had that Balthusian light, almost pink, as the sun neared the horizon, warming the foliage and setting the red-brick buildings of the old factory ablaze against the blue sky and grassy hills. It seemed then that time leaked like a mist out of the limestone around me. It seeped out of the prehistoric clay and lingered over the ponds. A night heron flew overhead, croaking noisily, and above the ponds swallows performed their acrobatics. There was something moody, desolate and marvellous about the abandoned buildings with their empty windows. The architecture of the old factory seemed emblematic of another time, another place, an evening almost a century ago when a kitten walked over wet bricks and looked up to watch the swallows.

Why History Gets Closer as You Age

A few days ago over lunch, a friend and I were talking about aging, and I submitted that the past gets more recent as you get older. "It's the flipside of the converging age paradox," I said. He asked me what that was, and I pointed out how, the older we get, the more that people who are younger than us "catch up" to our age. For example, if you are twenty and your younger sister is ten, then she is half your age. But when you're thirty and she's twenty, she gains on you: she's now two-thirds your age. When you are fifty and she is forty, she is four-fifths of your age. And so on. "Eventually," I said, "everybody ends up, more or less, the same age."

"But I'll always be older than my sister," he argued. "She'll never catch up completely." I agreed, but said that it hardly matters when your relative ages are so close. It's the same as historical perspective, I went on. I told him how, when I was a child watching old black-and-white World War II footage on the television, the 1940s seemed remote and primitive compared to the smooth, sophisticated world of the late 1950s. So here was another effect of the age paradox. The Allies had declared victory barely more than a decade before, yet for me, watching from my living-room rug, it might as well have been hundreds of years ago, because a decade was over twice my lifespan up to that point.

"The older you get, the closer you are to history," my friend observed. Exactly, I said. An event that took place ten years before you were born was equal to the entire length of your life when you were ten, but only half of your life when you turn twenty, and less than a third of your life when you turn thirty. Recent history, and all of history, gets closer to you the older you get.

It's a little like the distance paradox, my friend said—the one where, if you go half the distance towards a wall, and then half that distance, then half that distance, you approach the wall quickly, but in the end, you never quite get there. Like Zeno's Arrow, I said. He nodded. He then went on to offer his own theory, one that had to do with degrees of separation in time.

"We know history directly and intimately through people. Most of us have contact, through friends and relatives, with almost a century of history. If you take the future into consideration, the same thing applies. Some of the infants you know will still be alive almost a century from now. Its like degrees of separation, only in time. When I was young I met my grandmother, who had been born in 1850. Now I know a grandnephew who will most likely live at least eighty years, given today's life expectancy. When you add it up, in terms of generations, then, by proxy, I am one degree of separation from almost two hundred and fifty years of past and future."

ANCIENT BEINGS AND LIVING FOSSILS

I liked my friend's idea, and when we parted I began to think of it in terms of a personal connection with time. What would the giant sequoias on California's west coast tell us if they could communicate all the history they'd witnessed? What would animals that live longer than humans tell us? Parrots, large tortoises and crocodiles are among the longest-living animals, sometimes surviving longer than a hundred years in the wild. Humans would also have to be numbered among the longest-living animals, though only in special centenarian cases. The lengthiest documented human lifespan was recorded in southern France, where Jeanne Calment lived to be 122 years old. That would have given her direct, living contact with approximately three hundred years of human life, past, present and future. But in terms of longevity, the prize goes to tortoises. The oldest documented tortoise was named Harriet. She was rumoured to have been brought to England from the Galapagos by Charles Darwin in 1835, when she was only five years old. Later in life she was returned to the South Pacific, though to Australia instead of the Galapagos. She was a giant tortoise, and like all giant tortoises she grew for her entire life. When she died in 2006, at age 175, she weighed over 150 kilograms and was the size of a dinner table.

Plants, of course, completely outdo animals when it comes to lifespan, because their internal clocks tick that much more slowly. Nothing evokes the passage of time as eloquently as the growth rings of trees. We've probably all seen pictures of polished cross-sections of the trunks of giant redwoods adorned with arrows and little tags showing historical dates, such as the signing of the Magna Carta and the birth of Christ. A giant redwood's perspective on human history must be like a time-lapse film, or like the view of the fast-forward universe that you'd see if you fell into a black hole.

A few of the giant sequoias of coastal California have watched millennia come and go and are as gnarled and unyielding, if not as tall, as small mountains. The oldest known living redwood tree is 2,200 years old and is located in Humboldt Redwoods State Park in California. Two thousand, two hundred years amounts to 31 seventy-year human lifetimes. If we convert human years to sequoia years, then an average human lifespan of seventy years is just a little over 2.2 years for this old tree. Like Yggdrasil, the eternal world tree of Norse legend that supports the universe, giant redwoods seem immortal, surviving century after century and sustaining a forest world beneath their branches. Also like Yggdrasil, they are subject to distress. As it says in the Norse veda *The Gylfaginning*, "The Ash Yggdrasil suffers harms, more than men can imagine." A few decades ago, a giant redwood in California was struck by lightning and caught fire. Because redwood, particularly growing redwood, is not very flammable, the fire smouldered for months until it was extinguished by a snowstorm in the late fall. Fortunately, the tree was hardly affected.

For all their great age, redwoods are youngsters when compared to their elders a few hundred miles to the southeast. High in the White Mountains of California is a timeless forest of living trees so ancient they are hoary with time. Not tall trees, rarely growing higher than twenty feet, bristlecone pines nonetheless constitute a charmed grove of millennial bonsai. Most of them look like upended bits of living driftwood, or like the skeletons of mythical creatures. Their bleached branches and seemingly dead trunks, twisted and spiralled, resemble narwhal tusks or the mandibles of giant albino staghorn beetles. They gesture against the clear alpine sky like white antlers garnished with a few living branches of improbably verdant foliage. These gnarled pines, with their thick bases and weathered trunks, are miracles growing out of blanched scree, sand and boulders. One of them, with rings dating back 4,600 years, is the oldest tree in the world. A human lifetime, in bristlecone years, is barely twelve months long.

It almost seems as if these old trees, the sequoias and bristlecones, acquire a form of immortality by becoming partially inanimate, or simply by being so old. They contain so much dead tissue—bark, wood, dead branches—that they provide a second earth from which new life can spring. Like Yggdrasil, they rot and grow at the same time. The grey trunks of bristlecone pines that appear as monumental and lifeless as rock, so ancient they are almost geological, still manage to conjure forth new leaves each spring.

Up until 1997 the 4,600-year-old bristlecone wasn't just the oldest living tree but the oldest living plant. That honour now goes to a shrub discovered by scientists in a remote valley in southwestern Tasmania. The shrub is a member of the "King's holly" species, though this particular plant is a genetic freak, unable to produce seeds. It has been estimated to be forty-three thousand years old—thousands of years before humans entered North America. It's not tall, but it's quite large, covering two isolated river gullies. Yet even this Methuselah is not the oldest living *thing*. In fact, it's like a newly hatched tadpole compared to more recently discovered unicellular organisms.

In May 1995 scientists isolated a species of forty-million-year-old bacteria, *Bacillus sphaericus*, from the stomach of a bee encased in amber. The bacteria turned out to be in a state of suspended animation and, miraculously, scientists were able to revive them in a laboratory. These ancients were trumped in less than five years. In October 1999 250-million-year-old bacteria were discovered buried in ancient sea salt deposits beneath Carlsbad, New Mexico. They were also revived. They had survived inside their hard-shelled spores in the same state of suspended animation as the *Bacillus sphaericus*, except for millions of years longer. I wonder if they infected eurypterids. If only we could see the world the eurypterids knew. The urge to resurrect ancient creatures seems to be an almost universal fantasy, from Crichton's *Jurassic Park* to the work being done in Russia and Japan to clone mammoths using frozen DNA. But in one sense, in the form of living fossils, many ancient creatures have already been resurrected.

In New Zealand there is a reclusive, rarely seen nocturnal lizard about the size of an iguana and with the same kind of short dorsal spines. It has a large head and a lovely, delicately spotted skin decorated with misty, irregular stripes of tan and charcoal. This is no lizard, though; it is our only living link to the dinosaurs, and has remained unchanged since the Triassic era, 190 million years ago. It is a member of a family of reptiles, the sphenodontids, that arose at the same time as the dinosaurs. Continental drift marooned New Zealand just as the dinosaurs began to dominate, and the tuataras were left behind on their own island, isolated from the evolutionary and climatic changes that eventually brought about the demise of their cousins.

The oceans also harbour living fossils. Two species of stalked crinoids, identical to the ones that once waved their arms over the shallow oceans of the Paleozoic era, still exist today in the ocean at great depths. And the pearly nautilus of the Pacific, a kind of squid that lives in a coiled shell, is the last surviving member of the ammonites that died out with the dinosaurs. In 1939 the scientific world was astonished at the discovery of another prehistoric relic: a strange-looking plated fish with fins on the ends of rudimentary legs. It turned out to be a coelacanth, a creature virtually identical to its 420-million-year-old forebears, and its discovery was as shocking as if someone had stumbled upon a herd of triceratops.

If fossils are the three-dimensional, physical memories of the mind of evolution, then living fossils are both memory and resurrection. There is poetry here. Since the Muses are the daughters of memory, limestone must be soaked with inspiration. Even so, the past, like Orpheus's lost love, Euridyce, is locked away in time, the fearsome *Tyrannosaurus rex*, the long-tusked mammoths and the clockwork trilobites. W. H. Auden once wrote a poetic tribute to a fossil trilobite, his version of "alas poor Yorick," in which he mused upon what kind of world the trilobite once looked upon, and how the same eyes, now stony blind, gaze blankly at our own time. I think that Auden's resurrection of the lost world of the trilobite comes from the kind of nostalgia I myself am prone to, a nostalgia for the ancient past.

I am also nostalgic for the present, because it is so fleeting. It too will pass, and if the present moment is supreme, if it contains a once-in-a-lifetime happiness or achievement, then how much more poignant is it in light of its impermanence? Even a little moment of happiness (a *petit heureux*, as the French call it) can be saturated with nostalgia, like my idyll with the roses and clouds that summer afternoon in July, now borne away by time.

▲ ▲ ▲

The summer is waning. This afternoon I drove through Little Italy and saw cardboard crates filled with grapes stacked on the sidewalks in front of grocery stores. It's harvest time, and household vintners are pressing their grapes. September is the month of wine and corn. After supper I looked over the inventory of my wine cellar and realized that four bottles of red were mature. Like time capsules with expiration dates, they need to be opened and enjoyed. So now I'm going to do what I always do when a number of bottles are ready to drink—I'll hold a dinner party. It had better be soon, because I like to serve hors d'oeuvres and dessert on my patio, and this weather will not hold much longer. A process set in motion in the past, the bottling and fermentation of a vintage harvested decades ago, dictates my immediate future. All these years, in the cool darkness of my cellar, a slow, complex dance of colloidal tannins, sugars and esterification has gradually transformed the wine. I can hardly wait to open the first bottle and smell that heady bouquet of chocolate, honey, blackberries—and time.

Chapter Ten

The Echo at the Back Door of the Present

In the carriages of the past you can't go anywhere.
—*Maxim Gorky*

A Dinner Party

Everyone arrived at once. They brought flowers and bread and wine and strawberries and, after leaving their gifts in my kitchen, they went straight out the back door and into the yard. It was a warm, still evening, and though the sun was low in the sky it drenched the trees in a deep golden-pink light. Earlier, in the morning, it had rained, but the weather cleared up by afternoon. I opened a twenty-four-year-old bottle of Chianti Rufina to let it aerate in the kitchen, jammed a corkscrew in my pocket and, carrying a plate of smoked salmon in my left hand and a bottle of Barbaresco in my right, joined my friends outside.

Bruce and Michael were standing on the lawn looking at the banana tree (now more than chest-high), while Anne, Nicole and Sharon sat talking at the table, tearing off pieces of focaccia and dipping them in olive oil. Normally at this time of year, they would be fanning hornets away from their drinks, but even the wasps were co-operating. I had yet to see one, though September marks the highest population of yellowjacket wasps. (In England, during the height of the Battle of Britain in September 1940, the wasps were so plentiful that they spoiled the country outings of many Britons who tried to have picnics as they watched the aerial combat of German and British fighters.) I poured out the Barbaresco and carried two glasses over to Bruce and Michael. I was proud of my garden, which was still at its peak.

Both men were skeptical when I told them the banana tree would survive the winter, at least according to the little brochure that came with it. "Can you eat the bananas?" Michael asked. "I don't know," I said. "I think they're only ornamental. We'll see about both things, I guess." We talked a while longer, then rejoined the others at the table.

The Barbaresco went quickly, so I retrieved the Chianti from the kitchen and took it outside. The sun had just set and the sky was turning a lucid turquoise green. "Look, a hummingbird!" Nicole exclaimed. She pointed towards the mandevilla vine. There, like a tiny miracle, a ruby-throated hummingbird hovered and darted among the pink blossoms. Its iridescent throat glowed like an ember, and we could hear the hum of its wings. Then, like an arrow, it zoomed off.

There wasn't the slightest breeze. The smoke from Michael's cigarette hung blue in the air, wafting upwards in languorous arabesques. It was a magical evening, full of the energy of good friends in good spirits. I decided to use the vintage of the bottle, 1981, as a conversation starter. After I poured out the wine and we had each had a sip, I asked everyone to recount something remarkable they did during the year of the vintage. We used the bottle like a time capsule, releasing what it had captured in a long-ago summer.

Bruce volunteered to go first. He had been in a rock 'n' roll band that year, and he soon had us laughing at his wry anecdotes about concerts and buses and weird venues in small towns. Nicole went next. Nineteen-eighty-one had been her first year in Paris, where, during the summer, she had been spotted by a fashion designer and asked to model. Michael told us about his first one-man exhibition of photographs in New York City. Of all of us, he seemed the most nostalgic, sighing that he was better known in almost any country other than his own. Sharon had been a member of a performance-art troupe that year. They enacted stylized, slow-motion tableaux on the themes of bondage and liberation at alternative art galleries in downtown Toronto. In 1981, Anne recounted, she met the man who would become her second husband.

Under the stars we repeated the same ritual throughout the evening, each vintage yielding more memories and anecdotes, while moths circled my floodlights. It was as if, by opening the bottles, I was liberating the genies of our earlier, more splendid selves.

TIME CAPSULES

That night, as I dropped the wine corks and pieces of tinfoil and cheese rinds into a plastic garbage bag, I realized that I was constructing another time capsule, only this one was more like a piece of concept art. My collection of refuse was unique: a one-time assemblage of found art that I was hermetically sealing in plastic to be picked up and taken to a landfill site, where it would be buried so deeply that oxygen wouldn't be able to penetrate the bag, ensuring the preservation of the evening's particular detritus for decades, possibly centuries.

I mused that everything is a time capsule of sorts, anything that has any past, because it bears the stamp of its vintage throughout its whole existence. My kitchen table was made decades ago, it hasn't changed since then, and my cutlery is at least fifteen years old. Yet here they are, while the peonies that blossomed in my garden are gone, and the fledgling falcon is now an adult. That which is ephemeral seems most likely to be a prisoner of the past. Even the seemingly changeless things around us change: civilizations rise and fall, though pockets (Pompeii, Tutankhamen's tomb) are sometimes preserved like snapshots of history. But the concept of sealed cylinders containing memorabilia and messages meant for citizens of the future—time capsules proper—are an invention of the twentieth century.

◂ ◂ ◂

The first time capsule was designed by Westinghouse and buried in a special wall during the 1939 World's Fair in New York. Like a windfall for future archeologists, time capsules are meant to explain, illustrate and preserve for posterity our way of life, our culture and civilization. In that sense they are like passive time machines launched on a one-way journey into time with their votive collections of the everyday. They are an act of faith, faith that humanity will still be around centuries hence, and faith that the citizens of the future will be as interested in their past as we are in our own. Time capsules are like a note in a bottle, only the ocean the time capsule floats on is time.

There was something bullet-like about the sleek, cylindrical shape of the time capsule that Westinghouse fabricated for the New York World's Fair. It looked a little like a rocket, which it was, in the sense that time capsules are like artillery shells fired into the future, with the earth or concrete in which the capsule is buried acting as the barrel and the flow of time itself as the explosive charge. Even the metal skin that surrounded the contents of the Westinghouse capsule, separating them as it did from the present, seemed to place them in the anteroom of the future.

Because Westinghouse invented the concept, it also established the standard for what to put inside a time capsule. What would interest the archeologists of posterity? The company decided to group the objects in categories such as "Small Articles of Common Use," "Textiles and Materials" and "Miscellaneous Items." The list of contents was preposterously long—some hundred things, including an alarm clock, a fountain pen, safety pins, a slide rule, a watch, a makeup kit, children's toys, a package of cigarettes, a deck of cards, a chunk of stainless steel and asbestos, a package of various seeds, and money in coins and bills. There was also a microfilm library (although the celluloid that the microfilm was printed on will last only a hundred years at best) that contained novels, magazines, the *Encyclopaedia Britannica*, and a record of the history of art and science up to that point. How they fit so much into a cylinder measuring seven feet long by four inches in diameter is an achievement in itself.

A fountain pen, a watch, a nail file—how whimsical and sentimental, like the favourite furniture and jewellery that accompanied Egyptian royalty into their tombs. It's poignant, this fascination we have with surviving mortality by communicating with our distant descendants. Yet for all that, the future is still unknown, still possibly treacherous. Only the past is fixed. As the British essayist Sir Max Beerbohm once commented, "The past is a work of art, free of irrelevance and loose ends." When we bury time capsules we acknowledge that we will exist in someone else's past, and what seems so malleable now, the choices we make, the uncertainties we face, will become absolutely fixed in a past with no "loose ends."

THE BEGINNING OF TIME

There is an extraordinary painting by Paul Gauguin, from his Tahitian period, hanging in the Museum of Fine Arts in Boston. More like a mural than a single composition, it is almost three times as wide as it is high. The overall colour is a lush blue-green, and at first impression it seems more like an aquarium set into the wall than a painting. Dominating the centre is the almost naked figure of a young man or woman in a loincloth. The figure's toes extend close to the bottom frame, and his or her clasped hands reach to the top. On either side of the central figure, which divides the painting into two halves, are groups of the Tahitian beauties we are familiar with from Gauguin's other paintings of this period. We are likewise familiar with the sort of individuals who people the background. But there are some uncharacteristic elements.

In the extreme lower left-hand corner is a very old Tahitian, sitting with his head clutched in an attitude of despair. Opposite him, on the lower right side, is a baby lying peacefully on the grass. There are also dogs and kittens, and to the left of the central figure, an enigmatic votive figure, turquoise-hued, like an upright Buddha. The landscape is of a paradise—trees, mountains and a placid tropical ocean.

This painting, perhaps Gauguin's most mystical, is a chronicle of the human life cycle. Despite the benign, mild climate of this South Pacific Eden, or perhaps because of it, Gauguin was brought nearer to the ultimate truths of existence than he had ever been before. In the upper left-hand corner of the painting he wrote its title: *D'ou venons-nous? Que sommes-nous? Ou allons nous?* ("Where do we come from? What are we? Where are we going?") If ever an artist grappled with cosmology, the origins of the universe and, ultimately, ourselves, it was Gauguin with this work. Here on the shores of the South Pacific, among the simple lives of the Tahitians, he sought to pose the mystery of existence.

THE RING OF ETERNITY

A little over thirty years after Gauguin painted his masterpiece in Tahiti, the astronomer Edwin Hubble became director of an observatory that housed the largest telescope on earth—the Mount Wilson Observatory in Pasadena, California. It sat atop a mountain that was part of the same massif that spawned the bristlecone pines to the north. Like Gauguin, Hubble wondered where we came from, though for Hubble that question was linked to the larger question of where the universe came from. So, every night, he looked at the stars. But not just any stars. He preferred very, very distant collections of stars, which at the time were referred to as nebulae—we now call them galaxies. And Hubble knew he was looking not only farther than any human had before, he was also looking back in time.

Two years into his work at San Diego's Palomar Observatory, Hubble found himself confronting an enigma. There was a problem with some of the data, something didn't make any sense. It had to do with the way the galaxies were moving. It was wrong. Years earlier, astronomers had learned how to measure exactly how far away these inconceivably distant objects were. They had also discovered a way to determine which way a star was moving relative to the earth. It had to do with subtle variations in the speed of light: if a star was moving towards the earth, its spectrum "shifted" towards the colour blue; if it was moving away from the earth, its spectrum shifted towards red. The thing that perplexed Hubble was that the farther away a galaxy was from the earth, the more its light seemed to shift towards the red, which meant that all distant galaxies, no matter where he looked in the night sky, were accelerating away from earth. Hubble was more than mystified. If what he was seeing was true, then the planet earth, in a bizarre reversal of

Copernicus's discovery, was the repulsive centre of the whole universe. How could that be? Maybe there was something wrong with the optics of the giant telescope. Maybe his math wasn't right.

Hubble pondered this mystery for months until, in a flash of insight, he recalled a theory he had read in an article two years earlier. Written by a Belgian priest named Georges Lemaître, the article proposed that our universe started some billions of years ago with the explosion of a primeval atom. Hubble had an epiphany. He realized that here, in Lemaître's hypothesis, was a perfect solution to what seemed to be a contradiction. There was nothing wrong with his math or his observations. The universe *was* expanding, and it was doing so evenly and prodigiously. Earth wasn't at the centre of the expanding universe; it only seemed to be because every point in the universe was moving away from every other point, like raisins in rising bread dough. And if the universe was expanding outwards in this way, it must have at some point been much, much smaller. Running the universe backwards in time, Hubble understood that there was only one, inescapable conclusion: the universe *had* begun in a tremendous explosion, a "Big Bang," as the Russian physicist George Gamow later called it in 1948.

◂ ◂ ◂

Thirty-five years after Hubble's discovery, in 1964, Bell Laboratories contracted two communication specialists named Arno Penzias and Robert Wilson to try to improve microwave telecommunications signals by reducing background static. It seemed, at first, like a simple task. They were able to screen out almost every type of external noise they heard—radio noise, static electricity and even solar-flare static. But there was one type of noise that they just couldn't seem to get rid of. They tried everything to eradicate it, even cleaning the bird droppings off their antennae, yet the noise persisted. Anywhere or any time they pointed the antennae into the sky, the results were the same. In desperation, they called an astrophysicist at Princeton, who conjectured that maybe they were picking up background radiation from the universe itself.

With that idea in mind, Penzias and Wilson went back to their antennae and began to evaluate the consistency of the noise in all directions. It was identical everywhere, and it was clearly from a source beyond our own galaxy. After further analysis they realized, with mounting excitement, that they were eavesdropping on the birth of the universe itself. What was causing the background static was the primordial radiation left over from the Big Bang, like the sound of a bell that was still ringing, faintly, 13.7 billion years after being struck loudly at the very beginning of time. The irksome "noise" they had stumbled upon won them the Nobel Prize.

The Birth of Time

After looking at the evidence that Hubble and Penzias and Wilson presented, physicists concurred that time commenced at the beginning of the universe. They also concluded that there couldn't have been a "time before" the Big Bang. It turned out that the relationship between matter, energy and time in our universe is intimate—time came into being alongside the other dimensions. Here you might ask, "How could the universe have arisen from nothing? How could there *not* be a time before time?" These aren't naive questions. For hundreds of years, philosophers have struggled with them. In the late eighteenth century, Immanuel Kant decided that the birth of the universe must be a paradox, for how could anything arise out of nothingness? Nothingness, he said, couldn't create "a condition of being, in preference to that of non-being." In short, Kant came up against the modern reality—the universe is impossible and finite. St. Augustine also thought about the beginning of the universe, though he was closer to the modern scientific view. Linking time to its inception, he wrote, "The world was made, not in time, but simultaneously with time."

A helpful way to wrap your mind around what didn't come before the universe—the non-time before time began—is to think of it as identical to the period before you were born. At one point you didn't exist; then you did. The universe is like that, only without a parent. The nothingness that birthed our universe is so absolute that even death, the annihilation of a living being for all eternity, would be as life compared to it. This is what lies at the beginning and (as we will see) the end of the universe.

Okay, you might say, given the inconceivable absence of anything before the first moment of time, wouldn't there still have to be a *first moment*, a start to all of this? Science says no; the universe came out of less than nothing and had no first moment. Ask yourself if there is a final, smallest number that is just slightly, infinitesimally larger than zero. Try to find some number where you can stop and say, "There, that's the last number before zero." It can't be done. You can always keep halving a smaller number out of the previous until you meet infinity (or eternity, however you wish to look at it). Just as there is no final number, there is no first moment.

How, then, did moments themselves begin? And how did something come from nothing? This is where quantum physics comes to the rescue. At the level of quantum phenomena, which is a very strange and counterintuitive world, particles like electrons can pop into existence within the pure vacuum of interstellar space billions of miles from any stars. They literally appear out of nowhere, and it is this magic propensity that provides a clue as to how our universe began. Out of less than nothing, *within* less than nothing, where there was no time, no space, no matter, no "was," an infinitesimal blip switched on and the unimaginable occurred—a universe exploded into being simultaneously with the only element that could keep it expanding: time.

Yet according to physicists, even the presence of time itself was a bit of a fluke. They've modelled many other possible universes that could have arisen from a big bang—parallel universes where physics are slightly altered—and have found that some of them might even have formed without time. So we're lucky. As Paul Davies wrote in *About Time: Einstein's Unfinished Revolution*, "For reasons we know not, the quantum state of our universe, fortunately, *is* one of those very special states that permits time to emerge from this primordial jumble, as the universe 'evolves' away from the Big Bang, in a fuzzy and ill-defined way. And that is good news, because life in a universe without any sort of time would be difficult."

Now, 13.7 billion years after it began, time continues unabated. The present may be a vanishing threshold forever sliding into the future, but it has the entire history of the universe behind it, substantiating it. The past is the absent miracle that shores up the present. We are constituted by our history. Without the products of the past, without everything that history and prehistory has built—the mountains, the stars, the planets, the oceans and ourselves—the present would exist only as an abstraction within a vacuum, an airless, colourless trace moving like a solitary tsunami through an empty ocean of time. And we, without memory and past, would be vacant ghosts.

With the present being an impossibly small, possibly immeasurable fraction of time, time is almost 100 percent history. Time is almost entirely what was. But here's the kicker: what *was* doesn't really exist, except in our memories and the solid objects it has produced. And even they, in the end, will succumb to deep time, as the universe continues its evolution. Ultimately, when the fabric of the universe begins to unravel, when the atomic bonds that hold solid matter together break down after trillions of years, when even diamonds begin to dissolve (turning first into smooth spheres and then disappearing entirely), the emptiness of the past will become destiny.

THINGS YOU CAN'T TAKE BACK

> The past is only the present become invisible and mute; and because it is invisible and mute, its memoried glances and its murmurs are infinitely precious. We are tomorrow's past.
> —Mary Webb

September is almost over. Summer ended officially six days ago, on the twenty-second, and last night there was a frost warning. I put plastic over my basil plants and the big palm to protect them, though this morning there was no frost on the grass. Still, the banana leaves are looking a bit spotty, and while the flowers on my mandevilla are going strong, the leaves look a little lacklustre. It's a poignant season for someone who loves summer as much as I do. The celebration's over, the guests are leaving. This week alone I've seen two noisy V's of southbound geese. When I was mowing the grass a couple of days ago, I found a wine cork from my dinner party, part of the dwindling evidence of that marvellous night with my friends. The stopper from a time capsule whose opening is now in the past.

In one sense the past is very close to us. It is the perpetually open back door of "now." The present, in some entangled and complex way, is wrapped around the immediate past, and yet, at the same time, the past is always missing from it. The past just isn't there. Elusive, intangible, always pacing the present, it's one step behind; as soon as we turn to grasp it, it's gone, so that something that happened a second ago might as well have happened a hundred years ago for all that we can do about it. It is equally insubstantial, equally lost. This was a truth that was brought home to me, in a small but irritating way, last Friday afternoon when I locked my keys in the car.

It was rush hour and I had parked illegally in order to use a bank machine. The traffic was so heavy that I was trapped in my car at first and had to wait for a gap between cars before stepping out. As soon as I shut the door behind me, I realized that I'd left the keys in the ignition with the engine running. My mistake, a brief slip, was already part of the past. I couldn't take it back. Waiting for the towing company to come and break into the car, I thought of other moments where the instant division between present and past is equally irrevocable—transitory moments where the merciless past bares its teeth and holds on like a bull terrier.

I came up with the Waterford goblet knocked by an errant elbow from a counter above a marble floor; the cartoon character Wile E. Coyote lingering in the air after sliding off the top of a high mesa; the policeman's flashing light in your rear-view mirror; and the last glimpse of your house keys as they tumble down a sewer grate during a downpour. Driving home after the tow-truck operator rescued me, I thought of the past as the stone-faced customs agent who impounds your lip gloss or your butane lighter at the airport—you cannot argue with the past. There is no bartering, no deal-making. The past is absolutely bureaucratic.

Tonight, in my study, I can feel again the adamantine implacability of the past as I felt it this afternoon. The past is like a ubiquitous central vacuum that punctuates the entire universe with a micro-fabric of temporal black holes—a three-dimensional quantum sieve of suck. It's like a big drain, a funnel. Everything that falls into it is immediately carried away. You can say "now," and then you can say "now" again, but both "nows" are immediately in the past.

◂ ◂ ◂

When I pay close attention to the rushing divide between the present and the past, if I concentrate on that precise boundary where the universe and everything in it pour over the edge of "now" into the abyss of history, I imagine that I can sense it. The past is all around me, separated from me by an instant—the waft of a butterfly's wing, a slip of gauze. But it's my sense of hearing that somehow captures the present slipping into the past. When I listen closely enough, every sound—a ticking clock, the rustling of papers—seems to emit a faint, almost undetectable resonance as it slips into the immensity of the past. It's a sound beyond normal hearing, more like a studio sound effect than anything natural, and I'm far from sure that I hear it at all.

Perhaps this low-level, almost indistinguishable echo is like the "Hawking radiation" that leaks out of black holes. Not everything falls into black holes. At the edge of a black hole there is a barely detectable fizz of quantum particles that, because they are so light—almost massless—escapes its monstrous gravity. This outward escape of quantum particles is called Hawking radiation, after Stephen Hawking, who discovered it. It has great consequences for the future of the universe because it means that, after billions of years, black holes will simply evaporate, drained to nothing by the infinitesimal, but steady, loss of mass. This is a great contradiction of a law of physics called the Conservation of Information. According to that principle, all information contained in the universe has to be conserved, retained, even if transformed. The information in a piece of wood is contained in the molecular lattice of its cellulose. If the wood burns, the cellulose is converted into light, heat and carbon; nothing is lost. But if all the information that gets sucked into a black hole merely evaporates over time, then black holes represent a monstrous type of ultimate, cosmic death: the death of matter (and all the information contained in matter) itself. A past where even the past is annihilated.

Chapter Eleven

TIME TRAVEL

> I am afraid I cannot convey the peculiar sensations of time
> travelling. They are excessively unpleasant.
> —*H. G. Wells*, The Time Machine

A little over two blocks south of my house, there is a low escarpment,
about five or six storeys tall, that snakes several miles through the city. In
aerial photographs the cliff looks almost like a river as it meanders from
east to west across the grid of city blocks. One of the first and oldest
streets in Toronto, Davenport Road, runs along its base. Houses on the
north side of the street are angled into the bank so that their back doors
exit on the third floor. According to historical records, Davenport Road
follows the path of an old trail used by natives for thousands of years.
Before that the trail could only have been used by fish, because 11,200
years ago, at the end of the Wisconsinian glaciation, it was under water.

The escarpment is the old shoreline of an extinct glacial lake, Lake
Iroquois, that was twice the size of present-day Lake Ontario. Were a
catastrophic flood to resurrect Lake Iroquois, my house would be safe,
but most of the city, at least the part south of the old shoreline, would
be submerged. Only a few of the taller office towers in the financial
district would poke through. If my house could be transported eleven
thousand years back in time, then on windy nights I would be able to

hear waves crashing on the shore as they did when the glaciers had begun their last retreat.

My morning jogs have been glorious this week. The October leaves, like solar prisms, seem to be replaying all the sunny afternoons they soaked up during the summer. Every kind specializes in a different part of the summer spectrum—maples flame red and orange, the ash trees glow with deep, moody yellows, while the sumac thickets distill the fluorescent pink of a hundred sunsets. My jogging path takes me through a park perched on the edge of the Davenport escarpment. On clear, still days, I can see across Lake Ontario to the United States. For several mornings recently, when I've looked southwest, I've been able to see the mist from Niagara Falls, seventy kilometres away. It's a faint puff of what looks like smoke or steam, tethered to the horizon like an unmoving cloud.

The Niagara River tumbles over a limestone escarpment much higher than the earthen one that runs along the southern edge of my neighbourhood. At ninety metres tall and hundreds of kilometres long, it's one of the major landforms of the region. It extends in a great arc from Green Bay, Wisconsin, through upper Michigan into central Ontario, then down the Bruce Peninsula and through Niagara, finally petering out in upstate New York. As my father once did, I've learned to see landscapes in geological time-lapse, and the Niagara Escarpment has an extraordinary, almost cataclysmic, geological pedigree.

Because the continents float on a sea of molten magma, the land mass that now makes up Michigan and southern Ontario was once very far from where it is now. Six hundred million years ago, it was parked just south of the equator and covered with a tropical sea not unlike today's Caribbean Sea. But deep beneath the continental crust, a storm was brewing. A convection current launched from the centre of the earth began to spin the magma directly under this sea into a giant vortex. Like a cataclysmic version of Edgar Allen Poe's maelstrom, the magma whirlpool deepened and widened, drawing the rocky crust above down into it (imagine a thin film of plastic covering the vortex of a drain). Except that this was no transient event: the whirlpool lasted for millions of years. Eventually it created a bowl-shaped depression in the earth's crust that was overlaid with limestone deposits.

At its greatest extent, the lava vortex was eight hundred kilometres across, and it exerted its downward pull for three hundred million years. Then, mysteriously, it stopped. Afterwards, in a geothermal rebound, the bowl-shaped deposits began to rise for an additional two hundred million years. Finally the whole process ended.

The continent, with its slightly elevated limestone bowl, continued to drift northwards, and over millions of years the layers of limestone that formed the edge of the bowl eroded. Because they were canted up at a shallow angle, and because the top layer of limestone was composed of hard dolomite, a cliff face emerged over eons. At the time of the dinosaurs it was barely high enough to trip a baby *Tyrannosaurus rex*, but by the beginning of the ice age a million years ago, the escarpment was tall enough to make continental glaciers stumble.

"Time will tell," as the saying goes. It will, indeed. Geological time-lapse tells us truths that were once unimaginable. Everything around us, even the seemingly unmoving rock beneath our feet, is in transition. It is when we time-travel in our minds, animating inert landscapes, that the drama of life speaks to us.

A Seasonal Time Machine

When I was a child, every July and August resurrected for me the primeval, eternal summer of the age of reptiles. Snakes basked in the sun on forest paths near my home, and lizards with bright blue tails slipped through the ferns. In the pond, giant, antediluvian snapping turtles lurked. I was ten years old when I imagined that the seasons were like a Grand Canyon of time, that the journey from March to November took me through the same nine hundred million years as the geological journey from bottom to top of the world's deepest canyon.

Everything began on March 21. This was the first day of spring and, according to my dual calendar, the beginning of the Neoproterozoic eon. Here, at the dawn of life, the first unicellular animals arose. The pond was mostly clear of ice, and tiny, single-celled organisms proliferated invisibly in the shallows. I knew about them because the year before I had taken home a sample of pond water, put it under my brother's microscope and seen sleek, transparent creatures that used whips and moving bristles to propel themselves.

April was the beginning of the Paleozoic era, when the first crustaceans and fish began to stir in the ancient oceans. On bright, warm afternoons, schools of wild goldfish sunned themselves near the surface of the pond, and at night, in the shallows, the eyes of crayfish glowed like twin embers in the beam from my flashlight. Plants colonized the land during the Paleozoic, and, right on schedule, the first green shoots of wildflowers stuck up through the leaf litter in the woods.

Amphibians entered the scene during the Carboniferous period—in late April and early May by my calendar. The frogs began their mating trills, and I could hear them through my bedroom window on the first warm nights of May. The fiddleheads emerging in early May evoked the giant tree ferns of the late Carboniferous. By June tadpoles were wriggling by the hundreds in the pond, and even they obeyed the evolutionary edict of my geological calendar: they grew legs and dropped their tails in late June, transforming from aquatic to land animals. Amphibians gradually evolved into dinosaurs, and summer became the age of reptiles—July the Jurassic, August the Cretaceous.

Autumn, naturally, became the Cenozoic era, the age of mammals. The fat squirrels that buried walnuts in our backyard were glossy, and the neighbourhood cats looked sleeker and quicker as they stalked migratory birds in the hedges. All mammals seemed invigorated by the fall weather. Within the Cenozoic era, the late Tertiary period marked the height of the age of mammals. Some of these extinct behemoths reached extraordinary sizes, larger than elephants. The giant megathurium of South America, a kind of sloth, stood twenty feet tall. The glyptodon, from the armadillo family, was the size of an armoured vehicle. But global conditions were starting to cool. November and December brought the age of the glaciers, and then our own period of history, the Quaternary. During the first snowfalls in late November, I imagined herds of woolly mammoths gathering in the frosty gloom at the foot of glaciers.

Winter ended the yearly cycle, bracketing the beginning and the end of the journey of life through time, just as it did in prehistory seven hundred million years ago, when a glacial age almost ended the beginning of life on earth. This glacial age was apocalyptic; compared to it, later glacial ages were more like spring thaws. Simple multicellular organisms had barely gotten a foothold when glaciers spread out from the poles, just as they did only a few thousand years ago, but they didn't stop. They continued southwards until they covered the entire planet. All the oceans froze, capped with a kilometre-thick icy layer. If there had been intelligent life on Mars at that time, scientists there would never have bothered sending a rover to look for life on earth. Earth, as seen through their telescopes, would have been a brilliant white sphere, a barren planet that had been locked in a deep-freeze for millions of years.

And yet, life, hardly given the warmest of welcomes, survived. Bacteria, algae and prokaryotic organisms living near geothermal deep-sea vents and in hot springs, continued to exist for millions of years

until, finally, in a great thaw, the icy clutch of winter was broken. After that cosmic spring, life was reanimated in a renaissance that eventually changed the face of the earth. On my time-travel calendar, March 21 is like all the annual holidays rolled into one. It is nothing less than the celebration of the tenacity of life and its endurance over time. Now, in us, life can look back at its beginnings. If life was matter's dream, then consciousness was life's dream. It was only a matter of time.

TIME MACHINES AND WORMHOLES

> If you haven't found something strange during the day it
> hasn't been much of a day.
> —*John Wheeler, physicist*

Don't let anyone tell you there's no such thing as a time machine. I've seen one. It's the size of small city and it sits beside the Bay of Naples, in Italy. A few years ago, when I stepped through the northern gate of Pompeii, I stepped two thousand years back in time.

What astonished me was that Pompeii didn't look old—far from it. It was a surprisingly modern city, lacking only the voices of its citizens, the rasp of metal-clad wheels on cobblestone, and barking dogs. The architecture was elegant and sophisticated. The city blocks, or *insulae*, as the Romans called them, were laid out in grids identical to any North American city. And they had plumbing! Aside from electric light and internal combustion engines, Pompeii lacked nothing. At one point I lost track of the other tourists and spent at least half an hour alone, wandering through the streets, peering through the gates of marble-clad villas or investigating corner wine bars that looked as if their patrons had just gone down the street to watch some civic spectacle.

Even Vesuvius, the volcano that both destroyed and preserved Pompeii, still looms in the distance, a plume of smoke issuing from its peak. I couldn't get over the immediacy of the place; I became giddy with the sense of time travel. Later, after glutting my vision with impluviums, atriums, columns and statuary, I went to the train station and ate a grilled eggplant and cheese panini at a small café next door. It was there that I realized I had a feeling like jet lag, only this jet lag wasn't from crossing a time zone or two—it was from being transported through millennia. Perhaps, in my own way, I had experienced the same delirium that H. G. Wells' time traveller described.

◂ ◂ ◂

Curiously enough, science doesn't rule out the idea of time travel, especially into the future. In fact, the theory of relativity predicts it; if an object can attain speeds even half the speed of light, it will experience time warp. (As we know from our twin sisters, the twin who travelled into space and reached a high enough velocity returned to earth in the future.) But the notion of travelling backwards in time faces the seemingly insurmountable obstacle of time paradoxes, including the famous "grandmother paradox," which says that if you go back in time and murder your grandmother, you will never be born. This and other paradoxes, in and of themselves, seem to completely rule out time travel, and yet some contemporary physicists have neatly sidestepped them. Dr. Igor Dmitrievich Novikov, professor of astrophysics at Copenhagen University, has come up with an eponymous self-consistency principle asserting that a time traveller will never be able to create paradoxes because her actions in the past will be "over constrained" by the laws of space-time. Novikov believes that a time traveller would be prevented from murdering her grandmother, even if she made every effort to, by coincidental events that would always intercede.

Others, like Stephen Hawking, still believe that time travel to the past is not possible, given what we now know. Hawking has written a "chronology protection hypothesis" in which he argues that nature will always prevent travel into the past, much like the conservation of energy prevents energy from disappearing. Also, he points out, somewhat tongue-in-cheek, that we would already know if time travel into the past will be discovered in the future because we "have not been invaded by hordes of tourists from the future." Yet even Hawking does not absolutely rule out time travel to the past, and other physicists are even more enthusiastic about the possibility.

◆ ◆ ◆

The American physicist John Wheeler had always been fascinated by Einstein's theory of relativity. Even when his academic career at Princeton was interrupted by his participation in the Manhattan Project and Project Matterhorn B (the building of the atomic and hydrogen bombs respectively), he kept a corner of his mind busy tinkering with extensions to Einstein's formulae. When he returned to Princeton to teach full-time in the mid-1950s, he was able to devote much more speculative time to these ideas. Wheeler was particularly interested in the curvature of space-time, and in 1957 he realized that under special gravitational conditions, the structure of space might be able to form a passageway—a kind of shortcut—between two disparate regions. He called this passageway a "wormhole." Space-time physics hasn't been the same since.

Many of his colleagues scoffed at his theory, saying his wormholes contradicted some of the basic laws of physics. They cited Einstein and pointed out that wormholes were impossible because of the intimate relation between space and time. After all, they insisted, if the "shortcut" were long enough, it could conceivably permit faster-than-light travel, which was clearly an impossibility. But as the years went on, Wheeler's math held up. Yet wormholes remained a theoretical possibility only until the ultimate discovery of "black holes" (a name Wheeler coined as well) a little over a decade later. Black holes were mesmerizing for physicists, particularly when it came to how gravity and light behaved around them. Here all bets were off, at least as far as the laws of conventional physics went. Physicists soon recognized that because black holes bent space-time so radically, they could themselves be the entrances to wormholes connecting distant regions of space. But black holes annihilate everything that falls into them, and, even if they were an entrance to a wormhole, where would the exit be—a billion miles away? Or in some unthinkable, parallel universe?

The idea of wormholes has continued to fascinate scientists. Might wormholes someday be tamed? Might starships use them? Igor Novikov thought so, and he even went further. In his book *The River of Time*, Novikov speculates that at some point in the future it might be possible to build two huge gravitational fields that would create a wormhole between them. Why would we want to do this? Because, Novikov claims, a wormhole, after a bit of ingenious tinkering, could be turned into a time machine. And then he conjectures that there might be an even easier way to capture a wormhole, and it's right under our noses.

According to recent cosmological theories, our four-dimensional space-time universe is not what it appears to be. Apparently it has many other dimensions "curled up" inside the "quantum foam" (sub-atomic space-time) that underlies all matter. These are failed dimensions that, unlike the other four dimensions, didn't unfurl after the Big Bang. They survived, invisibly locked within matter throughout the universe, suppressed by the dominant dimensions of classical space-time. Like dimensional viruses suppressed by a cosmic immune system, they are biding their time until something or someone unlocks their potential. As well as holding these potential new dimensions, the matrix of the "quantum foam" contains some other surprises—tiny black holes. And wormholes.

Cosmic engineers could pluck a wormhole out of the quantum foam in our own backyard. In 1988, in a paper published by Michael Morris, Kip Thorne and Ulvi Yurtsever, the authors wrote, "One can imagine an advanced civilization pulling such a wormhole out of the quantum foam and enlarging it to classical size." Then, as Novikov blithely suggests, the wormhole could be stabilized and towed towards a large gravitational body, like a neutron star. (Attaching grappling hooks to such a will-o'-the-wisp would be one of the minor problems, no doubt.) Novikov would then park the wormhole vertically over the neutron star. One mouth of the wormhole would be lowered till it almost touched the surface, while the other would be raised hundreds of miles above the star.

Here's the clincher. Because gravity affects time—passing more slowly near the surface of a large planet and more quickly away from it—Novikov argues that eventually the two mouths of the tunnel would get out of synch. The greater the gravity and the longer the wormhole was left to develop its time differential, the greater the difference in time between one mouth and the other. Eventually, when enough of a temporal disparity had developed, Novikov proposes that the wormhole be dragged away and parked in an empty region of space. If the time difference between the two mouths was, say, two days, then as soon as the wormhole was parked, someone entering the mouth leading to the past would be transported two days backwards in time.

The main limitation to the idea of wormhole time travel is that you could never travel farther back in time than the date at which the wormhole started to operate. Sadly, visits to the Jurassic era would be out of the question. But Stephen Hawking's tourists from the future might well become a reality. In fact, I suspect that as soon as the wormhole was parked, maybe even before, tourists and who knows what else would begin to emerge from it. After all, the scientists of the future would have a leg up on the scientists who built the wormhole. They'd be able to look back over years of observations of the behaviour of the wormhole. Perhaps they would find ways of tweaking its performance, of extending its temporal range. The point is, the normal causal relationship between the building of knowledge over time from experience and observation could be inverted in a second. Cronos would be stymied.

◂ ◂ ◂

This brings us back to our paradoxes. What if a mischievous scientist from the future were to explain a Nobel Prize–winning technology to a scientist from an earlier age and the earlier-age scientist went on to win the prize? From the perspective of the future scientist, with access to history books, she knew that the earlier scientist was going to invent this technology anyway, but she short-circuited the process. She might not have been changing history, but she was subverting it. Both scientists would rely on future history being fed back into the past without any causality. Talk about intellectual property. And what if the scientist from the future gave the idea to someone else, and he or she got the Nobel Prize instead, altering history as in the grandmother paradox? Perhaps, as Novikov and some other physicists believe, none of these events could occur; something would always intervene to ensure that the law of causality would never be contravened retroactively. But there are other problems with time travel.

Right Time, Wrong Place

The intimate relationship between time and space is something that rarely occurs to novelists and filmmakers dealing with time travel. In H. G. Wells' *The Time Machine*, the world transforms around the protagonist while he remains stationary. If you think about it, though, time is also place. The co-ordinates of a specific time—say, Italy during the reign of Augustus—always include a place. But the fact that place and time are so inextricably connected presents an even more complicated problem for a time machine like the one Wells imagined.

Let's say you have built the first time machine, something the size of a phone booth. Because it's a prototype, it has a very limited range— something like twenty-four hours. Imagine that on a Wednesday afternoon, October 6 at 4:00 p.m., you decide to test your time machine for the first time. You step into the machine, strap on your harness and seat belt, make sure the airtight seals around the door are locked, and set the dials for 4:00 p.m. the day before: October 5. Then you cross your fingers, activate the chronological drive and *wham*—suddenly you're floating in space. The laboratory is gone, the city is gone, and the earth is gone. You look at the master clock in your time machine and, indeed, it does register 4:00 p.m. on October 5. But where is the earth?

Looking out of your time machine window (which, fortunately, you had the foresight to make airtight and pressurized in case of an emergency), you can see a blue-green planet about nine thousand kilometres away. Being a fairly savvy scientist, you realize that that planet is earth, and somehow you've missed your rendezvous with your laboratory. Earth, for some reason, is very far away. What happened?

There isn't much air in the time machine so you have to think quickly. Then, suddenly, you're hit with the terrible certainty that you've been a complete *dummkopf.* "Of course!" you exclaim out loud, "Why didn't I think of that?" What you've realized is that the earth moves in its orbit around the sun at 108,000 kilometres an hour, that our sun orbits the galactic centre at a speed of 792,000 kilometres per hour, and that our galaxy is moving relative to our local group of galaxies at about the same speed. Because time is also place, where you or your planet were a moment ago in the past is not where you or the planet are now. You and your time machine have hit the right time but the wrong place. Earth on October 5 was nowhere near where it was on October 6.

The old cliché about "spaceship earth" is quite correct—earth is moving faster than any rocket, though we don't get much of a sense of that speed when we're sitting in a comfortable chair reading a book, or strolling home from dinner at a local restaurant. The cliché should be changed to "timeship earth." Even if a time machine only went five minutes into the past, it would still simply disappear, not only because in our present time we couldn't see it, but because it would reappear five minutes back in time at that point in outer space, hundreds of kilometres away, where the earth had been five minutes earlier.

But is that really true? Perhaps I'm being naive. Although the jury is still out, there are some physicists who insist that special relativity compensates for the spatial difference. Here is where the counterintuitive weirdness of Einstein's theory reveals itself again, both to confound classic Newtonian physics and to save H. G. Wells' time machine from flying into space like the time machine in my example. According to some interpretations of special relativity, a time machine that follows a continuous timeline into the past or future will automatically travel through space as well. There's no need to worry about co-ordinates in three dimensions as long as you're on the timeline, which will always follow the curves of space-time.

Time Travel by Stopping in Time

What about a time machine that could idle, say, in a sort of temporal neutral gear—not quite in the present or the past or even the future—and stand still, motionless against the flow of time like a rock in a river, but more as if it were outside the dimension of time? I suppose that if you were able to stop, to let time flow past you, then the future would unfold around and ahead of you while you remained in stasis. Perhaps you would stay in one place, like a fixed date on the calendar, and sink into the past as the present moved increasingly ahead of you. Or if your time machine were just very slightly out of synchronicity with the flow of time, such a journey wouldn't be all that much different from what we already experience. Maybe you would take on a golden hue, like gold, or glow with the blue aura of Cherenkov radiation.

Are we not all like time machines of identity, moving forward into the future at the constant rate of time's passage? We pace time itself— "one second per second," as the scientists describe it. And we travel backwards too, at least in our memories. Deep sleep is a kind of time machine, though it only works for short hauls into the future. If people could be put into suspended animation, then the sleep effect of time contraction would be even more pronounced. If not exactly time travel in the orthodox sense, for someone revived after a century of suspension it might as well be.

Culturally we have been enthralled by the idea of time travel since H. G. Wells' groundbreaking *The Time Machine*. Other splendid novels such as Daphne du Maurier's hallucinogenic *The House on the Strand*, Jack Finney's *Time and Again* and J. K. Rowling's *Harry Potter and the Prisoner of Azkaban* have all dealt with the subject. As have hundreds of short stories, films and television movies.

◂ ◂ ◂

When I was fifteen my favourite television show was a time-travel series called *The Time Tunnel*. It aired, disappointingly, for only one season. The tunnel of the title was housed in a top-secret underground facility in the desert. There were no signs to mark its presence, no fences, only a road with an invisible gate that hinged the whole road downwards. Visitors drove down the ramp into an underground passage that led to the high-tech complex in which the time machine was housed. Behind them the road hinged up again, leaving no sign of the entrance.

The time machine itself was a tunnel whose black-and-white striped walls spun like an op-art whirlpool when the machine was turned on. The time travellers would simply walk into the tunnel and disappear, reappearing at their chosen destination in time. In retrospect I wonder if the whirlpool shape of the machine wasn't influenced by Wheeler's wormhole theory. If so, then the *The Time Tunnel* was the first visual representation of a wormhole in science fiction.

The Time Tunnel's main characters were two brave young men who had various adventures depending on their destination in time. By the end of the show's run, probably due to budgetary constraints, the protagonists ended up doing most of their time-travelling to the American Wild West of the nineteenth century. I suppose western sets were cheaper to lease. Very rarely did they go farther back in time or into the future, and eventually the show degenerated into a western.

At least the 1985 film *Back to the Future* had a sense of humour about time travel, especially in the appearance of the time machine itself: the souped-up De Lorean sports car. The most dramatic part of the film (borrowed from the 1984 film *The Adventures of Buckaroo Banzai*) was how the car/time machine travelled through time. The De Lorean had to race towards a brick wall or some other solid, immovable object and hope that it achieved the correct velocity to make the time-jump before it crashed. There's something whimsical and yet accurate about this—

the future, like an impervious wall, is an opaque barrier into which we cannot see, so we race headlong in the hope that we will penetrate it.

Car as Time Machine

Though not a modified De Lorean, my car, like all cars, is a time machine of sorts. This morning I was late for a dental appointment, so I used the car to gain time lost while I read a letter and watered the newly planted grass in front of my house. I drove three blocks south, then turned east on Davenport Road (the old Huron trail being the fastest route down-town). I went above the speed limit to make up for lost time, taking the risk that I wouldn't lose more time by being pulled over.

As I sped through the traffic, it struck me that my vehicle is a nexus of time. The glistening, lubricated metal shafts turning within sleeves of steel, and the engine itself, smoothly exploding bursts of incandescent gases in a controlled, industrial rage, are technologies that have remained unchanged since the nineteenth century. The electrical system that insinuates itself throughout the car, and is its nervous system, is from the twentieth century. And the gasoline that powers everything represents an even longer economy of time, oil deposits being the liquefied organic remains of plants and animals that are millions of years old. My pistons are fired by ancient sunlight, gathered by living matter, stored for eons in geological darkness and then exploded briefly into light again, though within another dark-ness—the mechanical midnight of the car's engine.

Then there's the final layer of time: the skin of fashion. My car is five years old, and its chassis represents an era of automotive styling that is almost passé. Not yet a living fossil, it is nevertheless a part of cultural history—an aesthetic time capsule from a previous decade. All of these factors—the concatenation of motion, history, prehistory and recent past—have interwoven so many layers of time within my car that it is, if not exactly a time machine, then a machine filled with time.

I enjoyed my brisk ride through the October sunlight and found a parking spot right in front of my dentist's building. Riding the elevator up to his office, I looked at my watch and saw that I was ten minutes late. That wasn't too bad, I thought, since my dentist is usually running behind schedule himself by this time of the morning. I opened the door to the waiting room and I could immediately tell by the expression on the receptionist's face that I was unexpected. "I have an eleven o'clock appointment with Dr. Kier," I told her. She consulted her appointment book. "That's tomorrow," she said. "Isn't this the eighth of October?" I asked. And she said, "No, today is Wednesday the seventh."

I was one day ahead of myself. I had somehow gotten a day out of synch earlier in the week, and it was only this collision with the real calendar that put me back on track.

Afterwards, with my unexpected free time, I went to a sidewalk café and ordered a cappuccino. While drinking it, I tried to recollect the exact moment or day that I'd skipped twenty-four hours ahead. I remembered that Monday had felt more like Tuesday to me for some reason, so perhaps a subtle, unconscious association had triggered the time lapse. But in the end, I thought, how we measure time is arbitrary. We could have thirty-six 40-minute hours in a day, a week could be ten days long, and our calendar could have twenty months. What *isn't* arbitrary is that time, like gravity and mass, is a fundamental quantity. No matter what we do, or where we go, we glide into the future at a rate of one second per second.

◂ THE FUTURE ◂

Chapter Twelve

The Shape of Things to Come

> The future is already here. It's just not very evenly distributed.
> —*William Gibson*

Indian summer arrived yesterday, right in the middle of October. A few cicadas must have survived the cold nights last week, because in the heat of the afternoon they sang as loudly as on any August day. I hadn't heard the cicadas for weeks, and their rasping buzz sounded almost wistful—the swan song of summer. During my jog this morning, I couldn't make out the distant plume of vapour from Niagara Falls because the air was filled with a fine blue mist. It was as if sky pigment were flaking off in a dusty powder, and it tinged the far landscape blue and indistinct, like an impressionist painting. I've seen this blue mist before, not only in the city but in the country as well, as far away as the Appalachians. It isn't pollution and it isn't the smoke from hundreds of leaf fires.

I like to think of it as time vapour, as if time, normally invisible, thickens and reveals itself in this particulate haze. There is a nostalgic, slightly somnolent ambience to these misty fall afternoons. They remind me of the autumn afternoon in the Catskills when Rip Van Winkle fell asleep after bowling with the ghosts. Maybe his stupor wasn't just a narcotic effect of the enchanted liquor he drank, but a consequence of inhaling too much time vapour from the mountain air. Like someone in a coma who, at least from his or her perspective, wakes up in the future, so did Rip Van Winkle awaken to a country transformed by revolution. Who would have predicted such change in a mere two decades?

◢   ◢   ◣

As Yogi Berra once reportedly quipped, "It's tough to make predictions, especially about the future." The future has a way of throwing curves at even the most conservative prognostications, and as a result the history of prediction is strewn with disastrous prophecies. We can look back with irony at Neville Chamberlain's declaration of "peace in our time" as he waved the ill-fated treaty with Hitler. Not every prediction is wrong, though, and indeed, weather forecasting seems to be steadily improving, even if the long-range forecasts are still sometimes uncertain. According to today's five-day forecast, there may be a frost this weekend, so I've arranged for my palm tree to be picked up and taken to the greenhouse for the winter.

Planning for the future is a basic condition of existence. We arrange for mortgages with twenty-five-year terms, we schedule vacations and we make payments towards the university education of six-month-old babies. We even plan for our own nonexistence—a paradox, and probably the most palpable evidence of our abstract relationship to time. All life prepares for the future, even if it doesn't do it abstractly, as we do. Plants are constantly thinking ahead. My rhododendrons have already set their flower buds for next year. The horse chestnuts in the park have ripened, and the branches are laden with hundreds of spiked green globes, every one cleaving open and containing two chestnuts, like polished wooden geodes mated belly to white belly, a future tree within each. The squirrels have stashed their hoard of black walnuts in my yard and even in my garage; I keep finding walnuts lodged earnestly in the woodpile.

On that rainy day last April, when I went to my publisher's and we discussed the timetable for the production of my book, we agreed that there would likely be galleys (the first typescript version of the manuscript) by February, provided I delivered the manuscript in September. Well, here it is almost November already and I'm still writing. If my publisher gets impatient, maybe I'll just quote Einstein, who once wrote, "The distinction between past, present and future is only an illusion, even if a stubborn one."

◂ ◂ ◂

Even though most scientists are great skeptics about anything remotely paranormal, physicists don't even skip a beat when they claim that the past, present and future exist at once. The Einstein quote about the illusory distinction between the three realms of time comes from a letter he wrote to console the widow of his friend and associate Hermann Weyl. Einstein himself was only weeks from death and was wrestling with the problem of the present. In conversation with the philosopher Rudolph Carnap, he said that there was "something essential about the now," though that essential core lay "just outside the realm of science." To Weyl's widow he seemed to be intimating that her husband still lived, and would always live, somewhere in the timescape. He knew it was possible.

But if the timescape does indeed exist, it seems to be dominated by the one-way flow of time, and that flow, the flow of "now," is terrifically fast—a billion billion femtoseconds per second. How could anything cross such a bottleneck from the past or the future? Oddly, there is an outside chance of it happening. A handful of scientists, most notably

William Unruh, Theodore Jacobson and Renaud Parentini, have been publishing reports about space-time behaving like a fluid. They are particularly interested in black holes because of the way black holes contradict the general rules of physics. Even light, the fastest thing there is, gets sucked into the monstrous gravity of a black hole. Yet, as I discussed earlier, in a phenomenon known as Hawking radiation a small number of photons escape the hole, driven out by the very energy that sucked them in.

Jacobson and Parentini believe that Hawking radiation is evidence that something extraordinary could take place—that ripples travelling through space-time could, with enough speed, move upstream of a quickly flowing medium, much the way that a stationary rock in a river creates a little series of upstream ripples around it that move against the flow of the current. The unstated implication of this theory is that perhaps the flow of time itself, though tremendously fast, could also retroactively transmit similar sorts of ripples "upstream." If, as most physicists believe, the future already exists alongside the present and past in the timescape, then perhaps a large enough event in the future might be able to broadcast ripples backwards against the entropic flow of time towards the future. What form those ripples might take, or if they'd even be detectable, is wide open to speculation, but it seems to provide a mechanism for a kind of physical precognition.

◀ ◀ ◀

Many philosophers have contemplated the idea of the future influencing the past, though in more practical ways. Aristotle was one of the first to come up with the notion of entelechy, or the acme at which the entire potential of a thing's or a person's essence is realized. The thing or person moves towards and is influenced by it. Entelechy is similar to teleology, the doctrine of final causes, defined as that which lies at the end of tendencies, goals, aims, directions. In other words, the end of the means. More recently, a number of technologically minded thinkers, including Ray Kurzweil, have come up with the idea of a future singularity, a decisive, watershed event in the evolution of technology that will change what it means to be human. Some think that this singularity (a word that seems borrowed from black-hole terminology) will occur when the first replicator, a microscopic nano-robot capable of building other nano-robots, is created; others believe that the singularity will arrive with the advent of artificial intelligence.

Interestingly, many of these individuals are convinced that a kind of entelechic or teleological field surrounds this event in the future. For them, our present age is converging irrevocably towards a singularity and, what's more, the singularity is so massive it casts a reverse shadow, backwards in time, from the future, through the present and into the past. The poet Percy Bysshe Shelley was thinking along the same lines when, in his 1821 book *A Defence of Poetry*, he wrote, "Poets are the hierophants of an unapprehended inspiration; the mirrors of the gigantic shadows which futurity casts upon the present." This singularity is, I suppose, not that much different from manifest destiny, except writ large for all of mankind. If you are fascinated, as I am, by the notion of a singularity, you'll have to take these theorists on faith. Keep in mind, though, that scientists have got things fantastically wrong in the past.

The Victorian era was a golden age of science that laid down the infrastructure for the achievements of the twentieth century, but its fearless enthusiasm also produced claims that turned out to be dramatically amiss. In 1874 Sir J. E. Erichsen, one of England's most preeminent surgeons, wrote, "The abdomen, chest, and brain will forever be closed to operations by a wise and humane surgeon." Who could have predicted neurosurgery and heart transplants back then?

Twenty years after Erichsen's pronouncement, Albert Michelsen, one of the scientists who measured the speed of light, declared the end of physics. "It seems probable," he said, "that most of the grand underlying principles have been firmly established." He then went on to quote Lord Kelvin, who apparently once mentioned that "the future truths of physical science are to be looked for in the sixth place of decimals." In other words, if you're a young aspiring scientist, don't bother getting a physics degree—there's nothing left to discover. Less than two decades after Michelsen's premature pronouncement, X-rays, radioactivity and relativity were discovered.

And still eminent scientists predicted that certain possibilities were forever closed. In 1932 Albert Einstein said, "There is not the slightest indication that nuclear energy will ever be obtainable." Ten years later, underneath the squash courts at the University of Chicago, Enrico Fermi fired up the world's first nuclear reactor. (But Einstein gets the last laugh, at least in terms of bogus predictions. His high school teacher once told Einstein's father, "It doesn't matter what he does, he will never amount to anything.")

Contemporary scientists would never make the mistake of saying they know all there is to know. On the contrary, they are fond of repeating Ralph W. Sockman's adage, "The larger the island of knowledge, the longer the shoreline of wonder." Like the Victorians, they believe in the ultimate power of science, but they appreciate that science is far from finished. It seems to have a limitless ability to reveal new worlds and create wonders. Of course, they continue to make predictions, even as they realize that the likelihood of being right is far from certain.

◆ ◆ ◆

Stanley Kubrick based his film *2001: A Space Odyssey* on Arthur C. Clarke's premise that the moon would be colonized and civilian space liners would have regular service between the earth and the moon by 2001. In 1969 lunar exploration was in its infancy. Thirty-two years no doubt seemed like a conservative estimate. But the future isn't what it used to be. Clarke later pushed forward his 2001 date by ten years, and he also prophesied that astronauts would land on Mars by 2021, nine years sooner than NASA's best guess.

A future project that might surpass the achievement of moon bases and Mars landings, at least on an engineering scale, is the construction of a space elevator. Consisting of a rigid tube assembled in stationary orbit (built downwards at the same time as it is built outwards, in order to compensate for gravity and centrifugal force), such a structure is, apparently, quite possible. When complete, passengers would simply ride it up into space. In 2004 Bradley C. Edwards, head of the Institute for Scientific Research, envisaged the existence of a space elevator by 2020. Authur C. Clarke was a bit more ironic about the idea. He said that a space elevator "will be built about ten years after everybody stops laughing."

The advent of robots is yet another magnet for futurist prognostications. In 2003 Marshall Brain, creator of the How Stuff Works website, forecast that robots would perform at a human level of skill in most manual jobs by 2030, though Helen Greiner, the chairman of the corporation iRobot, put it a little later, at 2034. In 1997 the computer scientists who organize the yearly RoboCup soccer games were confident enough to claim that by 2050 a team of robots would beat the human world champions in soccer.

Of course, as robots become more complex, their intelligence will begin to approach our own. Many computer scientists and science fiction authors believe that artificial intelligence—the attainment of human-level consciousness—is inevitable. In another of his predictions made in the year 2001, Arthur C. Clarke forecast that artificial intelligence (AI) would be attained by 2020. Ray Kurzweil came in a year earlier at 2019, while Hans Moravec, the visionary computer scientist and mathematician who's in a position to know just how complicated human consciousness is, has his money on 2050.

Nanotechnology, one of the fastest-rising fields of research and development, is a wholly new frontier in science and, reminiscent of X-rays and radioactivity, something that wasn't even imagined a few decades ago. The grail of nanotechnology—the building of a cell-sized programmable robot that can build replicas of itself—garners a wide range of predictions regarding its advent. In 2001 Arthur C. Clarke put the date at 2040, though the U.S. Army's Future Force Warrior Project recently estimated that by 2020 nano-machines embedded in body armour would be able to transform the properties of the armour from flexible to bulletproof, filter out biological weapons and even treat wounds. And for the record, Clarke also predicted the successful cloning of dinosaurs by 2023.

◄　◄　◄

Who knows exactly when, or even if, any of these wonders will come about? I remember watching newsreels in the 1960s that showed men flying in jet packs, which the commentator said would be as common as cars within a decade or so. The future is slippery, especially when it comes to the adoption of technology. Virtual reality smacked of the future, but who could have predicted cyber-sickness? It is the inventions we didn't expect at all that have turned out to be the biggest. A decade before the Internet, very few would have guessed just how pervasive it would become. And technology keeps throwing new devices at us at an ever-increasing, sometimes overwhelming, rate. It seems that you either adapt to the future or you become its victim. Even science cannot tell us what's in store, though not for lack of trying.

Pierre-Simon de Laplace, one of the great mathematicians of the scientific renaissance that spanned the eighteenth and nineteenth centuries, conjectured that science and mathematics would eventually be able to predict the future perfectly. In his treatise *Théorie analytique des probabilités*, written in the early decades of the nineteenth century, he explained how:

> Given for one instant an intelligence which could
> comprehend all the forces by which nature is animated
> and the respective positions of the beings which compose
> it, if moreover this intelligence were vast enough to
> submit these data to analysis, it would embrace in the
> same formula both the movements of the largest bodies in
> the universe and those of the lightest atom; to it nothing
> would be uncertain, and the future as the past would be
> present to its eyes.

Laplace was voicing the hubris of scientific rationalism at one of its most exciting periods. In this passage, he envisaged how a God-like intelligence would be able to calculate the future, given a thorough enough knowledge of the past and present. It speaks much of Newtonian and Cartesian idealism, where elegant formulae paralleled the perfect harmonies of the golden proportions. But the universe has become a much stranger and more turbulent place in the intervening decades. Here, at the beginning of the third millennium, scientists make highly reasonable speculations rather than bald declarations. Kurt Gödel's unprovability theorem took the wind out of the sails of absolute knowledge in the mid-twentieth century. A few decades later came the mathematicians of chaos theory—among them Edward Lorenz, who discovered the "butterfly effect," which is more or less the ability of a very small event to have catastrophic consequences. It turns out that accurately and absolutely predicting the behaviour of large numbers of anything, be they atoms or stars, is pretty much impossible, at least on the specific level.

If an omniscient scientist were able to have complete access to a universe in which he could stop time, and if that same scientist, like Laplace's hypothetical intelligence, had a colossal supercomputer that could register the position of every particle in his universe and then calculate the future trajectory of every atom, electron and quark, what would happen when the universe was restarted? According to chaos theory, the universe would obey his calculations for about one, maybe two seconds before unforeseen turbulence set in. No matter how complete our knowledge or how perfectly predictive our calculations, we can never, ultimately, forecast for more than a second or two what will happen in such a large region. Time is equivalent to turbulence in such deterministic systems; it introduces randomness. We can know the general picture of the universe, we can even predict its ultimate fate with utter certainty, but we cannot know what will happen along the way.

Twilight of the Dawn

My palm tree was picked up yesterday afternoon. Two men carried it through my garage and out to a white truck parked in the lane. I accompanied them, helping to keep the leaves from tearing on the doorways. In the lane I could see that the truck was already partially filled with other potted tropical plants: mandevilla vines, hibiscus shrubs and a spreading bougainvillea. They were crowded in like refugees being evacuated before an invasion. Just in time, as it turned out. The attack, in the form of a killing frost, came last night. Early in the evening, as ice crystals began to sparkle on my lawn, I put a makeshift greenhouse—clear plastic stapled over a slender wooden frame—over my basil plants. But this morning, despite my precautions, I noticed that some of the leaves had wilted. The banana tree looked disastrous. Its collapsing leaves were mottled with large brown patches.

Although it was sunny this afternoon, it was also cool, the late October sun too low to warm my skin. Most of the trees in the neighbourhood have lost their leaves, though the towering willow in the backyard across the street is still green, as if it were sheltering the last remnants of summer in its leafy depths. I put on my jacket and walked over to the park. The air was dusted with the scent of dry leaves, and there was a faint, intoxicating background of leaf smoke. High piles of bronzed oak leaves were on the street in front of several homes. I riffled a hand through one of the piles and noticed that, like snowflakes, no two oak leaves were the same. At one house, a man was decorating his front porch for Halloween, stringing thick artificial cobwebs over the banisters and pillars. His next-door neighbour had placed a diminishing set of bright orange pumpkins on his steps, starting at the bottom with a pumpkin the size of basketball and finishing at the top with one as small as a tennis ball. The pumpkins worked like an optical illusion, making his steps appear deeper and longer than they actually were.

In the park, dogs chased balls and sticks thrown by their owners and children screamed in the little playground. Each of the trees had a wide circle of brown leaves beneath it. Even though it was only five o'clock in the afternoon, the light was already starting to fade. Tonight we set the clocks back. Over the next few days, people will have stationary jet lag—a direct, physical consequence of our chronometric abstraction. Monday morning rush hour will witness a few more fender-benders than usual. But it's not just the end of daylight saving. The gloom closes in more quickly this time of year because the encroachment of darkness accelerates in mid-autumn, as the shape of our orbit around the sun conspires with the tilt of the planet to speed up the shortening of the days.

On the way home I bought a pumpkin at the little grocery store around the corner and carried it home on my shoulder. I like Halloween. It's one of the few purely secular and nocturnal celebrations in North American culture. But as the children are out trick-or-treating, employees in retail stores will be burning the midnight oil to make sure that Christmas displays are in the windows when the doors open next morning. The retail economy has always been locked into a cyclical calendar, except now it's looking further and further ahead. Fashion designers bring out their seasonal lines six months in advance. Magazines arrive in stores and mailboxes at least a month ahead, and by the time the month printed on their covers has rolled around, they are off the shelves. But the future will not be harnessed. It has its own agenda.

◂ ◂ ◂

The future opens up into possibility. Anything can happen. A meteor could streak from the sky and land in the middle of the street next to the park. A poor labourer in South Africa could unearth a giant diamond on a dirt road and have his life changed forever. The field of potential that is the future is also fallow ground for fantasy. We live in its thrall. "The future enters into us," wrote the poet Rainer Maria Rilke, "in order to transform itself in us, long before it happens."

Just as there is a deep past, there is also a deep future, one that in terms of human destiny is beyond individual comprehension. As a species we are just getting started. H. G. Wells had an inkling of our destiny when he wrote in *The Discovery of the Future*, "The past is but the beginning of a beginning, and all that is and has been is but the twilight of the dawn." It's really a question of how much time we have, and according to cosmologists there are billions and billions of years ahead for this universe. All the time in the world.

◂ ◂ ◂

Today, October 31, I cut back the dead stems of the peonies and ornamental grass, leaving the bare earth of my garden beds. Even the weeds have shrivelled away. The only green left in my yard is the deep emerald of the lawn, the viridian leaves of the bamboo, the mossy green of the rhododendron and the paler green of the big yuccas under the kitchen window.

After lunch I sat outside and carved the pumpkin with a thin-bladed knife. Every year I cut the same design—a wide, grinning demon's head crowned in flames. The motif works well with the yellow-orange of the candlelit pumpkin's interior, and I get compliments from some of the trick-or-treaters. "Your pumpkin's cool," one little girl said last year. I have a bowl of candy by the door ready for dusk, which is when the first toddlers will appear in their oversized costumes. As the evening wears on, the trick-or-treaters will get older, and by ten or eleven o'clock, teenagers in quickly improvised get-ups will clean up what's left of my hoard. My pumpkin will glow malevolently into the night until, sometime past midnight, the light in its head will go out.

Chapter Thirteen

STEALING ETERNITY

> Swiftly the years beyond recall
> Solemn the stillness of this fair morning
> I will clothe myself in spring clothing
> And visit the slopes of the Eastern Hill.
> By the mountain stream a mist hovers
> Hovers a moment, then scatters
> There comes a wind blowing from the south
> That brushes the fields of new corn.
> —*T'ao Ch'ien*

In 1986 two cosmologists from Oxford University—John D. Barrow and Frank Tipler—published an astonishing book called *The Anthropic Cosmological Principle.* Within its painstakingly researched 706 pages, they argue that, in a strange and wondrous way, the destiny of life on our planet is intrinsically linked to that of the universe. They write, "The realization that the possibility of biological evolution is strongly dependent on the global structure of the Universe is truly surprising and perhaps provokes us to consider that the existence of life may be no more, but no less, remarkable than the existence of the Universe itself."

It seems that our presence here is no accident. If any of the basic elements of the universe were even slightly different, say Tipler and

Barrow, human life would not have arisen. And they go further. They demonstrate that because of these razor-thin constraints—the precise relativities between basic forces such as light and gravity as well as the availability of certain elements—intelligent life, and specifically human life, was inevitable. They make this contention even though the statistics seem to argue against human life having occurred. According to the algebra, human life is inevitable, but only in one location (and possibly two) in the entire universe. Everything Barrow and Tipler looked at, from atomic bonds to the composition of stars, pointed in a single direction. Eerily, hair-raisingly, everything was precisely tailored to create on our planet one instance of carbon-based life—ourselves. The odds against our existence mean that the presence of life on our planet is almost supernatural. The universe, they suggest, exists for us.

Time, it seems, also has a hand in this remarkable convergence. Not only is this the only possible universe in which we could have existed, this is the only possible time. They write, "For there to be enough time to construct the constituents of living beings, the Universe must be at least ten billion years old and therefore, as a consequence of its expansion, at least ten billion light years in extent. We should not be surprised to observe that the universe is so large. No astronomer could exist in one that was significantly smaller." These aren't just speculations. They are based on the same kind of spit-and-polish mathematics that underlies nuclear reactors and planetary motion.

Using the same reasoning, Tipler and Barrow then look billions of years into the future to see what the logical conclusion of their anthropic principle will be. They maintain that because the universe was "fixed" to create intelligent life like ourselves, it was also designed to nourish us at each stage of our evolution. So, as our technology and intelligence evolve, we will discover that every constituent of matter will become useful to us at every successive stage of our progress, as if it had been designed that way. And apparently it was. Eventually, life will expand to fill first our universe, and then "all universes that are logically possible."

Barrow and Tipler don't invoke God to explain their extraordinary form of manifest destiny, though their assertions seem to require precisely that kind of faith. (Such assertions are as close as science gets to the notion of divinity.) But they do foresee a problem with our eventual omniscience. No matter how like immortals we become, we will never be able to reverse the arrow of time. The universe will eventually end. What will happen to life then?

◂ ◂ ◂

This past week has been cold, almost like winter. On the few nights when the sky is clear, the stars have an icy clarity—sparks struck from the black flint of space. The seasonal march of the constellations has taken Andromeda from just above the horizon, where I saw it in June, and parked it directly overhead. Nestled in the curve of the Andromeda constellation is the faint glow of the Andromeda galaxy. Aside from being the only galaxy visible to the naked eye, it is also almost the mirror image of our own, the Milky Way. Not only do both galaxies have a spiral shape, both have the same tilt relative to the other. Astronomers on a planet located in the Andromeda galaxy, looking at the Milky Way, would see something very similar to that which our astronomers see when we look at them. The sister galaxies are connected in another way as well. They are nebulaic ballroom dancers that are circling a common centre of gravity, drawing nearer to each other at the rate of fifty miles per second. In a few billion years the Andromeda galaxy will loom twice as large in our sky.

These time scales relativize my own existence. I find them inspiring and reassuring. As the physicist Freeman Dyson wrote in his book *Infinite in All Directions*, "Letting our imagination wander among the stars, we too may hear whispers of immortality." By day, the window on the galaxies is replaced with a grey November sky—a featureless, ashen plain that scrolls from horizon to horizon. This is the season that ends seasons. The bare trees look like abandoned scaffolds left over from a carnival that has yet to be disassembled. But the Austrian pine down the street beside George's house is as green as it ever is. It has a low, spreading crown and its long needles are set in thick, bushy clumps. When it catches the late-afternoon sun, even on the coldest winter days, it is refulgent with semitropical green that remains steadfast despite the temperature.

▴ ▴ ▴

In terms of my calendar of life on earth, the seasons have caught up to the present. For me, the first snow marks the beginning of the glacial age and of our own era, the Holocene. There is something aqueous, and a little clinical, about the grey, shadowless light of cloudy November afternoons. Bare branches, the armatures that supported the stage sets of summer foliage, are exposed, and the soil is naked. The glacial ages marked the migration of humans out of Africa northwards into Europe, and they must have huddled in early winter geographies not unlike this one. The deserted November landscape has a post-apocalyptic quiescence. What few remaining islands of green there are, like the Austrian pine, seem to glow. My eyes rest there, slaking their thirst for the colour of life.

On a cool afternoon earlier this week I saw a little cloud of small moths dancing in the air above the table on the patio. It was a mating flight, even though the temperature was only a few degrees above freezing. Still, there they fluttered, a fragile yet hardy species eking out an existence at the final margins of life before winter. November is the month at the end of time—and it is timeless. A photograph of my yard would look the same whether it was taken in in November, December, March or early April. My bedraggled rose bush has one final bud; if we get a few warm days, it may blossom. There is bravery in this evacuated panorama.

GÖTTERDÄMMERUNG

Only a few religions incorporate the idea of Armageddon—most notably Christianity, with its doctrine of the End of Days. But for most of them doomsday is not final—a new order always rises out of the ashes. It seems that true fatalism only existed in early Norse mythology. The Vikings created a belief system that dealt not only with human mortality but also with the mortality of the universe, which they believed would be destroyed in the final battle of the gods. As set forth in the *Gylfaginning*, their mythology was a precocious forerunner of our current knowledge of the fate of the universe.

You'll recall that, according to the *Gylfaginning*, the universe was embodied by a giant ash tree: Yggdrasil, or the world tree. In his book *Hammer of the North*, the Norse scholar Magnus Magnusson writes, "Yggdrasil holds the fabric of the universe together, a living and sentient being." Magnusson then goes on to describe the "fearful torments" that the world tree suffered, noting that "Yggdrasil reflected the parlous condition of the world, a world that was flawed and doomed from the start."

Yggdrasil is fertilized with celestial hydromel, and its three great roots draw nourishment from three sources. One root taps into Urd's Well, a fountain of youth tended by the three Nornir, the goddesses of fate who rule past, present and future; another root draws water from the Hvergelmir Fountain, the source of all water (in Niflheim); while a third root taps into the Fountain of Mimir in the world of the giants.

It is from Urd's Well, the fountain of youth, that Yggdrasil derives its longevity. The secret of time, guarded by the Nornir, appears to be the great tree's elixir. Yet despite being nourished by time itself, Yggdrasil is doomed. At the top of the great tree, a gold cock scans the horizon to warn the gods if it sees the giants mounting an attack that will signal the beginning of the end of the gods. The other lookouts are a giant eagle surveying the entire world from Yggdrasil's branches and a hawk perched on the eagle's beak, ready to fly wherever necessary. The *agent provocateur* in this limited ecology is a mischievous squirrel, who constantly runs up and down the trunk, creating discord between the eagle and the serpent that lives at the roots of the tree.

◂　◂　◂

Our present-day scientific version of the end of everything is on a scale that would be incomprehensible to the Vikings. I think, though, that they would be impressed with both its fatalism and its apocalyptic grandeur. Will there be gods to battle the giants at the end of our universe? Perhaps. Happily, doomsday for the cosmos is a long, long way off, trillions and trillions of years away, and the Anthropic Principle tells us that we have an extraordinary future before us.

Hans Moravec, founder of the world's largest robotics program, at Carnegie Mellon University, has lingered thoughtfully in the corridors of the future. Tempering his astonishing imagination with scientific rigour, he has painted visions of the future that are as fantastic as they are invidiously plausible. In his seminal book *Mind Children*, which takes a look at the future of artificial and human intelligence, he chronicles a destiny where inconceivably vast engineering projects and powerful computers combine to reshape planets and the basis of life itself.

One of his more extraordinary scenarios envisages what might happen if a sufficiently large and sophisticated computer were able to simulate the whole surface of our earth—not just at a large scale, but down to the atomic level. Everything—dirt, coral, human consciousness and flies—would be replaced with perfect copies of itself. The total information contained in every cell, every atom, would be extracted and transferred to a computer bank. Human beings in such a simulation would be indistinguishable from you or me.

All this could take place without our even being aware of it. (Of course, if you were a little paranoid, you might think, "How do we know that we aren't already simulations, imprisoned in a superintelligent computer like the pod-bound humans in *The Matrix*?" But that is an unanswerable question, one about which we could speculate for years without solving its riddle. For now, let's assume that we're not.) Moravec knows from his experience with today's complex simulations, such as planning the trajectory of unmanned space probes to other planets or modelling nuclear explosions, that simulations obey the basic laws of physics, one of which states that time is symmetrical. A simulation can be as easily run backwards as forwards.

So, Moravec asks, once the simulation of earth has reached complete saturation—with every atom, every quark, captured in a replication—why not run the whole planet backwards in time? As each past inhabitant of the earth was resurrected, he or she could be uploaded into a new, immortal body. All the people who ever existed could live again, their infirmities cured and their minds restored. In this way, Moravec claims, even our most distant ancestors would be able to share our fantastic destiny. As he sees it, "Resurrecting one small planet should be child's play long before our civilization has colonized even its first galaxy."

Perhaps Judaism has it right: the righteous will be resurrected. Although in Moravec's vision the not-so-righteous will rise up again as well. The point is, if we survive as a species, if we don't succumb to our own imperfections, our future literally has no limits. Running time backwards on planet earth, if indeed this ever happens, will be only the first in a series of almost inconceivable scientific and engineering accomplishments—the harnessing of stars, the towing of black holes for use as power—that, given the trillions of years left to us, will inevitably produce superbeings with the powers of gods . . . or perhaps a single entity stretching from one side of the universe to the other.

The Irish physicist J. D. Bernal had an intimation of how the rise of superbeings might come about. Predicting that humans would transform themselves beyond recognition, he wrote, "Finally, consciousness itself may end or vanish in a humanity that has become completely etherealized, losing the close-knit organism, becoming masses of atoms in space communicating by radiation, and ultimately, perhaps resolving itself entirely into light." This adaptation, Bernal said, would allow these post-humans to colonize vast areas of otherwise inhospitable space. He goes on: "As the scene of life would be more the cold emptiness of space than the warm, dense atmosphere of the planets, the advantage of containing no organic material at all, so as to be independent of both these conditions, would be increasingly felt." Since Bernal published his visions of the future of humanity, other scientists have speculated on what post-humanity may look like. It is certain that it will be nothing we can now imagine. But there are inevitabilities about which we can speculate with some assurance. And Barrow and Tipler make a convincing argument that eventually life will spread to inhabit the entire universe. It will be then, when no other frontier is possible, that the only door locked to these godlike beings will be the one that opens to eternity. For the universe has an expiration date.

▲ ▲ ▲

The end will come in one of two ways: cosmic "heat death" (which is really more like the "big freeze") or the "big crunch." Science can't tell

219

us which one will win out because the weight of the universe is at the borderline between the two possibilities; it might continue to expand indefinitely, overcoming the contracting effects of gravity, or it might stop expanding and begin to collapse. The first scenario, heat death (or death from lack of heat), sees the stars snuff out one by one, and matter itself disintegrating until the temperature of the empty universe reaches absolute zero in the final darkness. The second, the big crunch, is the reverse of the Big Bang. Here gravity prevails. After expanding for billions of years, the universe starts to contract and ultimately collapses upon itself, imploding in a fiery annihilation that will be the mirror image of its birth.

If, as Thomas Gold proposed, time begins to run backwards in a contracting universe, then for its inhabitants birth will become the final moment of life. But these inhabitants won't know time is reversed. Their thoughts will flow logically and naturally in the new direction of time as our own do, and the universe will appear to be expanding, just as our own does. But its end will come all the same.

THE ENDGAME

> Worlds may freeze, and suns may perish, but there stirs
> something within us now that can never die again.
> —*H. G. Wells*

Can total annihilation be deferred, or even avoided? How do we snatch eternity from the jaws of a finite universe? Hans Moravec, among others, has wrestled with cosmic mortality and come up with an ingenious solution that just might work. It all hinges on the paradox of Zeno's Arrow—if you keep halving the distance that the arrow has yet to travel, the arrow will never arrive. This turns out to have practible applications. What if, Moravec asks, the universe is headed for heat death? How could an infinite amount of time be squeezed from a finite amount of matter and energy?

Moravec's answer is clever. He says that our descendants could build a tremendous battery consisting of two giant mirrors that faced each other. Moravec proposes that a beam of photons be endlessly reflected between the two mirrors to harness the energy of light. The photons would push the mirrors farther apart and the energy from the moving mirrors would power civilization. Moravec writes, "The idea is to use about half the energy in the battery to do T amount of thinking, then wait until the universe is cold enough to permit half the *remaining* energy to support another T, and so on indefinitely."

But what if the universe contracted instead? In this case Moravec again proposes mirrors, only now they would surround a stored vacuum. As the universe contracted, the vacuum would yield increasing amounts of energy. He writes, "A subjective infinity of thought might be done in the finite time to collapse by using this growing power to think faster and faster as the end draws nigh. The trick here is to repeatedly do an amount of thinking T in half the remaining *time*." Of course, when Moravec refers to "thinking," he means the complex information-processing that it would take to maintain such advanced beings within their real and virtual worlds.

Freeman Dyson has also contemplated how the endgame might play out is. Dyson is famous for his visions of fantastic engineering projects in the distant future. Perhaps his best-known scheme is the Dyson sphere, where a living star is enclosed within a giant globe and all the star's energy is harvested for the benefit of a civilization living on the sphere. When first proposed, this idea was so compelling and so logically inevitable that astronomers began looking for Dyson spheres as a method of determining whether there was intelligent life elsewhere in the universe. Occasionally, they argued, stars should sporadically dim and then wink out, evidence that an advanced civilization had reached the Dyson-sphere stage. So far, no such stars have been found.

But even Dyson spheres would not save a dying civilization at the end of the universe—stars will run out of fuel long before that. If heat death is indeed the ultimate fate of the universe, then Freeman Dyson has another trick up his sleeve. He proposes using the cooling temperature as a way to defer mortality. Our descendants, either superbeings or some sort of ultra-intelligences, would have to radically conserve energy in order to carry on. If they could, then they might be able to survive in a "subjective infinity," as Moravec calls this sleight-of-hand immortality, but only if they were able to speed up their thought processes. Dyson maintains that the cold could be used to dissipate the heat inevitably generated by such vast information processing— thinking generates heat. But as available resources dwindled, these beings would have to ration their energy. He suggests that they might go into long periods of hibernation. Subjectively, they'd never be aware of their downtime, their thoughts would resume without interruption as soon as they reawakened, and the increasingly longer periods of hibernation would go unnoticed.

Frank Tipler, one of the co-authors of *The Anthropic Cosmological Principle*, has also wrestled with these questions. In his 1994 book *The Physics of Immortality*, he suggests that a superbeing who had grown to encompass the entire universe would use all available energy to process its thoughts, which would themselves include simulations of all possible worlds. But, appreciating that its own fate was tied to that of the universe, what would the ultra-brain do to survive? As we now know, even *it* wouldn't be able to supervene the second law of thermodynamics, no matter how intelligent or omniscient it was.

Tipler's answer is not unlike Moravec's: the faster you think, the faster you act, and the more living you can fit into a smaller slice of time. The race does go to the quick, and it is inevitable that the cognitive speed of beings in the future will certainly outpace anything today. Since the longevity of existence is equivalent to the speed of thought (a Femtonian lives a million years during one of our seconds), Tipler argues that as the thinking process of the ultra-brain sped up, it could use the immense energies and unusual physics of a collapsing universe to increase the subjective speed of thought infinitely—the ultimate escape. If time is indeed infinite inwards, and the femtosecond within the nanosecond has an endless series of smaller and smaller divisions within it, then perhaps that inward abyss of time might be the key to our future, and our survival.

Even before the end of the universe, there are other pitfalls along the way that might end it prematurely. There is some speculation that when the first black hole evaporates through Hawking radiation, it might destroy the universe. This is because each black hole contains the end of time. It's possible that if space-time collapses in the singularity of a black hole that completely evaporates, the collapse will spread outwards and destroy everything else along with it. To forestall such a catastrophe, Barrow and Tipler suggest that future intelligences could simply keep dumping matter into those black holes that were teetering at the brink of complete evaporation. They write, "Thus ultimately life exists in order to prevent the Universe from destroying itself!"

In the end, the interlocked fates of life and the universe hinge on life's immortality. It is our only hope. But then a new dilemma arises, one that takes me back to my childhood bedroom, where I wrestled with the opposed fates of mortality and immortality. The idea of existence without end is pretty frightening, so much so that, for some, extinction might seem preferable.

The Deep Future

The timeline for our universe, if it keeps expanding and ends in eventual heat death, has been worked out in detail by physicists, astronomers and cosmologists. Regardless of whether or not our progeny expand to fill it, the universe will run down. Tipler and Barrow (who refer to the universe that contains not only our visible universe but also all possible universes with a capitalized "Universe") predict that in one thousand billion years, new stars will cease to form. Billions of years after that—or ten billion billion years from now—90 percent of the stars in the universe will have evaporated, while the remainder will have been sucked into massive black holes. In ten million, billion, billion, billion years, all carbon-based life forms will become extinct.

You'd think that would pretty much be the end of things, but within the barren, dark emptiness of this future cosmos, inside matter itself, non-carbon-based life would be blazing its own bright future. From now on, the universe's timeline becomes so staggering that we have to convert to trillions in order to economize on words. In a trillion, trillion, trillion, trillion, trillion, billion years, the massive black holes that once formed the centre of galaxies will evaporate. Yet there will still be plenty of matter and energy available to sustain whatever beings exist.

Long after black holes have evaporated, if they don't take the rest of the universe with them, the timeline becomes so incomprehensibly huge that we have to resort to powers of ten to write out the numbers. The black hole deadline that I mentioned above would be written as ten to the power of ninety-nine, or in notation, 10^{99}. The next major event in our timeline would be during the early middle age of our universe. Trillions of years after the lights have gone out, a strange encounter might take place.

According to the mathematics of the Anthropic Cosmological

Principle, in 10^{800} years, our descendants will encounter the descendants of *Homo sapiens* that have arisen elsewhere in the universe. It seems Carl Sagan was a bit optimistic about the abundance of extra-terrestrial beings. When this poignant meeting happens, intelligent life will be close to saturating the entire universe, though the endgame will still be trillions of years ahead.

The final years of the universe, when the temperature has dropped to absolute zero, will likely occur sometime after 10^{1500} years, though here the timeline becomes speculative. This is indeed a long-lived universe. But if, instead of expanding, the universe begins to contract and is ultimately annihilated in the "big crunch," there might not be so much time left. If gravity wins the tug-of-war, the universe might last only twenty to thirty billion years longer. Hardly any time at all. What is certain is that, at 13.7 billion years old, our universe is young. And still, human life has already arisen, perhaps precisely because we need the rest of this time, these potential billions or trillions of years, to expand and to occupy the universe and all parallel universes that make up the Universe.

Our history has been marked by expansion and discovery. The urge to explore oceans and cross nameless deserts has constantly spurred us on. Ultimately, it seems, we will visit the stars and the galaxies beyond, and when we do, we will become the gardeners of the universe. But the tending will be mutual, for it appears that the universe is both garden and gardener itself.

The management and use of time may turn out to be our greatest achievement, far outshadowing any giant engineering projects of the distant future. Time is the final resource, and the universe, railing against the end of time, has put all its chips into our eventual ability to cheat death, not just for our heirs, but for the universe itself.

Chapter Fourteen

THE SECRET OF THE PINE

Nothing in the world lasts,
Save eternal change.
—*Honorat de Bueil*

Last week, on a dark, cold afternoon, an ambulance pulled up in front of George's house. The attendants went in with a gurney and soon re-emerged with George. He was walking, with some difficulty, his arm braced by one of the paramedics. I realized that he had refused to lie on the stretcher. They got into the ambulance and left. Since then the lights in George's house have been off, and I fear things did not go well at the hospital.

This week a For Sale sign appeared in front of my Portuguese neighbours' house, and yesterday morning their real estate agent slipped a brochure under my porch door. The neighbourhood is changing. Even the houses are transforming. Several neighbours with young children have expanded their homes with additions and new decks. On most days one or two contractors' vans are parked on the street.

It snowed last night, as this morning the roofs of the houses and the cars were dusted with white. By noon the snow had melted, though it was gloomy and cold all day. But just before evening fell, the sun came out. Its rays were almost horizontal as it crested the roofs of the buildings in the west. The sunlight had a warm tinge, and the bricks of the houses across the street were lit up as if they were glowing red-hot, fresh from the kiln. My Austrian pine (I must admit to proprietary feelings, even if it isn't on my property) was also lit up, its thickly set combs of needles as green as any June forest. It radiated a timeless calm and seemed to harbour daydreams in its lobed canopy.

RADIANT TIME

Because time's flow has no three-dimensional direction, it's hard to picture how time ramifies, how it slides from past to future. Yet time moves neither up nor down, left nor right, east nor west. Trying to grasp time's motion, or lack of motion, has been one of the most difficult things I've ever tried to conceive. The best I can do is create metaphors, which may not accurately reflect what time is, but which at least lead me towards a more essential grasp of its intrinsic nature.

Last March, when I stood beside the rustling bamboo, time felt like a wind that blew through everything. That sensation captured the ubiquitous nature of time, how it manages to insinuate itself into the smallest atom and the largest galaxy at once. It also revealed time's invisibility and its power to change the fabric and shape of whatever it blows through, like waves of wind rippling fields of summer grass. But the metaphor didn't get at the unidimensional character of time, the fact that time doesn't actually move through this world at all. Or, if it *does* move, it moves unlike anything else in our universe.

This afternoon, though, looking out at the old Austrian pine across the street, watching the sunlight that seemed to incandesce its foliage, I had another sensation of time. It came to me in an image of rain falling on a still pond. The ripples spread from each drop in a randomly even pattern of overlapping, expanding rings. Then I imagined the surface of this pond doubled, so that there were two transparent surfaces, one just above the other. I could see the rain splashing on the second pond as well, with its own pattern of ripples. Then I pictured another surface laid over the first two, and then another and another, until they were countless and filled all space. Now the ripples from each drop propagated not in flat rings but in expanding, transparent spheres within spheres, radiating through all the layers. Time, I thought, didn't flow from the past towards the future, but from inside of everything, at once, everywhere.

It was the old pine that congealed this vision. In the sunlight it looked dusty, almost pointillistic. Just for an instant, I could see the millions of expanding, transparent circles of time spreading out of the tree before they became microscopic and invisible. As they faded, they merged into the world—into the other trees, the buildings, the clouds, the sky and the earth. A purple finch flew into the pine and started up its melodious song while a tabby, stalking beneath, paused to look up at the bird. These creatures, both wild and tame, myself, these buildings, all joined in the net of time.

Everything sheds time in a steady emission that swells out of every atom, every leaf, every human being—even out of empty space. That's why the old pine, with its evergreen halo of sun-soaked needles, seems beyond time. It, and me, and all of us, are soaked in Chronos. Perhaps time is more like a sourceless, uniform inner light. Its outward-flowing ripples are so small, so fine, they are undetectable. Perhaps the fountain at the heart of time is the infinitely divisible "now," the "now" that is a billion billion "nows" within itself. Every second is infinite—a millisecond in the second, a nanosecond in the millisecond and a femtosecond in the nanosecond. It all blossoms, swells out from the centre of everything at once. We shine with time. True, time's arrow points in one direction, just as the needles of the pine radiate outwards from their branches or rays from the sun point in one direction, but time's grain is directionless. Time's arrow points everywhere at once, and all of creation glows with time.

It is here that our future lies, not ahead but within. If each second contains a near eternity, then are we not, in one very real sense, already immortal? And even though we are as unconscious of our immortality as an elephant is of the ants that crawl over its hide, we nonetheless exist within eternity, and our lives, however brief, stretch for countless eons within each minute, infinities within each hour.

Acknowledgements

I extend my initial thanks to my publisher, Iris Tupholme at HarperCollins Canada, for her continuing support and assistance. As well, I thank my editor, Jim Gifford, and managing editor, Noelle Zitzer, who oversaw final production.

Barbara Gowdy also provided invaluable editorial advice during the preparation of the manuscript. In addition, thanks go to Rob Firing and his team.

This book was assisted and influenced by many, including Marnie Jackson, Ken Alexander, Martin Levin, and Margaret Atwood. Grateful acknowledgement is also made to the authors whose work is cited in the book and listed in its bibliography.

In addition, I am indebted to my agent, Bruce Westwood of Westwood Creative Artists, who provided much of the time to write this book. Finally, I thank Carolyn Forde and Natasha Daneman, also of Westwood Creative Artists, for all their assistance.

SELECTED BIBLIOGRAPHY

Ackerman, Diane. *A Natural History of Love*. New York: Vintage, 1995.

Amis, Martin. *Time's Arrow*. New York: Harmony Books, 1991.

Associated Press. "After 130 Days of Cave Life, A Return to Glare of the Sun." *New York Times*, May 24, 1989.

Augustine, Saint, Bishop of Hippo. "On the Beginning of Time." *The City of God*. Translated by H. Bettenson. Harmondsworth: Penguin, 1972.

Augustine, Saint, Bishop of Hippo. *Confessions of St. Augustine*. Translated by R. S. Pine-Coffin. Baltimore: Penguin, 1961.

Aveni, Anthony. *Empires of Time: Calendars, Clocks, and Cultures*. Boulder, CO: University Press of Colorado, 2002.

Barnes, Ernest. *Scientific Theory and Religion*. Cambridge: Cambridge University Press, 1933.

Barrow, John D., and Frank J. Tipler. *The Anthropic Cosmological Principle*. Toronto: Oxford University Press, 1986.

Benjamin, Walter. "On the Concept of History." *Illuminations*. Edited by Hannah Arendt and translated by Harry Zohn. New York: Harcourt, Brace & World, 1968.

Bernal, J. D. *The World, the Flesh, and the Devil: An Enquiry into the Future of the Three Enemies of the Rational Soul.* New York: E. P. Dutton, 1929.

Borges, Jorge Luis. "A New Refutation of Time." *Labyrinths.* New York: New Directions, 1964.

Bureau of Labor Statistics. *Time Spent in Primary Activities and Percent of the Civilian Population Engaged in Each Activity, Averages Per Day by Sex, 2006 Annual Averages.* United States Department of Labor. www.bls.gov/news. release/atus.to1.htm

Cano, R. J., and M. K. Borucki. "Revival and Identification of Bacterial Spores in 25- to 40-Million-Year-Old Dominican Amber." *Science* (May 19, 1995). www. sciencemag.org/cgi/content/abstract/268/5213/1060.

Chesterfield, Philip Dormer Stanhope. *The Letters of the Earl of Chesterfield to His Son.* Edited by Charles Strachey. London: Methuen & Co., 1925.

Christianson, David. *Timepieces: Masterpieces of Chronometry.* Toronto: Firefly Books, 2002.

Couzin, Jennifer. "How Much Can Human Life Span Be Extended?" *Science* (July 1, 2005). www.sciencemag.org/cgi/content/full/309/5731/83.

Darling, David. *Deep Time.* New York: Delacorte Press, 1989.

Davies, Paul. *About Time: Einstein's Unfinished Revolution.* New York: Simon & Schuster, 1995.

Davies, Paul. *The Last Three Minutes.* New York: Basic Books, 1994.

Dennett, Daniel C. *Consciousness Explained.* Toronto: Little, Brown, 1991.

Donne, John. "The Sun Rising." *The Love Poems of John Donne.* New Rochelle, N.Y.: Peter Pauper Press, 1934.

Dyson, Freeman. *Infinite in All Directions: Gifford Lectures Given at Aberdeen, Scotland, April–November 1985.* New York: Harper & Row, 1988.

Einstein, Albert. *Ideas and Opinions.* [*Mein Weltbild.*] Edited by Carl Seelig. Translated by Sonja Bargman, New York: Bonanza Books, 1954.

Gangi, Angie. "Harriet the Tortoise Dies at 75." *ABC News* (June 23, 2006). www.abcnews.go.com/Technology/story?id=2112240.

Gasquet, Joachim. *Joachim Gasquet's Cézanne: A Memoir with Conversations.* Translated by Christopher Pemberton. London: Thames and Hudson, 1991.
Gleick, James. *Chaos: Making a New Science.* New York: Viking, 1987.

Gould, Glenn. *Glenn Gould Hereafter.* Bruno Monsaingeon (Director). Paris: Idéale Audience International/Rhombus Media, 2005.

Grossman, Lev. "Forward Thinking." *TIME Magazine* (October 3, 2004). www.time.com/time/covers/1101041011/story.html.

Hawking, Stephen. *A Brief History of Time.* New York: Bantam Books, 1988.

Hofstadter, Douglas R. *Gödel, Escher, Bach: An Eternal Golden Braid.* New York: Vintage Books, 1980.

Huxley, Aldous. "Seasons." *The Cicadas and Other Poems.* London: Chatto & Windus, 1931.

International Science and Technology Center. "ISTC Supports International Research in Paleobiology." www.istc.ru/istc/sc.nsf/stories/mammoth.htm.

Jacobson, Theodore A., and Renaud Parentani. "An Echo of Black Holes." *Scientific American* (December 2005).

James, William. *The Principles of Psychology.* London: Macmillan, 1890.

Khayyám, Omar. *Rubáiyát of Omar Khayyám.* Translated by Edward FitzGerald. Portland, ME: T. B. Mosher, 1899.

Kiderra, Inga. "Backs to the Future: Aymara Language and Gesture Point to Mirror-Image View of Time." uscdnews.ucd.edu (June 12, 2006). www.ucsdnews.ucsd.edu/thisweek/2006/june/06_12_backs.asp.

Kingsley, Charles. *Yeast: A Problem.* London: J. M. Dent & Sons, 1912.

Kurzweil, Ray. *The Age of Spiritual Machines: When Computers Exceed Human Intelligence*. New York: Viking, 1999.

Lawrence, D. H. "Song of a Man Who Has Come Through." *Look! We Have Come Through*. London: Chatto & Windus, 1917.

Laumann, Edward O., John H. Gangnon, Robert T. Michael, and Stuart Michaels. *The Social Organization of Sexuality: Sexual Practices in the United States*. Chicago: University of Chicago Press, 1994.

Leslie, Mitchell. "The Man Who Stopped Time." *Stanford Magazine* (May/June), 2001.

Lucretius. *De Rerum Natura*. Translated by. A. D. Winspear. New York: Harbor Press, 1956.

Magnusson, Magnus. *Hammer of the North: Myths and Heroes of the Viking Age*. London: Orbis, 1976.

Marcus Aurelius, 121–180. *Meditations*. Translated by A.S.L. Farquharson. New York: Everyman's Library, 1946.

Marvell, Andrew. "To His Coy Mistress." *The Poems of Andrew Marvell*. London, Lawrence & Bullen, 1892.

McLuhan, Marshall. *Understanding Media*. New York: McGraw Hill, 1965.

Melville, Herman. *Battle-Pieces and the Aspects of the War*. New York: Harper, 1866.

Melville, Herman. *Mardi and a Voyage Thither*. Edited by Harrison Hayford, Hershel Parker and G. Thomas Tanselle. Evanston, IL: Northwestern University Press, 1998.

Moravec, Hans. *Mind Children: The Future of Robot and Human Intelligence*. Cambridge: Harvard University Press, 1988.

Morgan, Ted. *Literary Outlaw: The Life and Times of William Burroughs*. New York: Avon Books, 1988.

Morris, Michael, Kip Thorne and Ului Yurtsever. "Wormholes, Time Machines, and the Weak Energy Condition." *Physical Review Letters* 61: 13 (September 1988).

Mumford, Lewis. *Technics and Civilization*. New York: Harcourt, Brace & World, 1963.

Nietzsche, Friedrich. *The Gay Science*. Translated by Walter Kaufman. New York: Vintage Books, 1974.

Novikov, Igor D. *The River of Time*. Cambridge: Cambridge University Press, 1998.

Oates, Joyce Carol. *Marya: A Life*. New York: Dutton, 1986.

Pakenham, Thomas. *Remarkable Trees of the World*. London: Weidenfeld & Nicolson, 2002.

Popper, Karl R., and John C. Eccles. *The Self and Its Brain*. New York: Springer International, 1981.

Qain, T'ao. *T'ao the Hermit: Sixty Poems by T'ao Ch'ien (365–427)*. Translated, introduced and annotated by William Acker. London: Thames and Hudson, 1952.

Routledge, N. A., "Achilles and the Tortoise: A Consideration," *Eureka* 27: 24–6 (October 1964).

Russell, Bertrand. *A Free Man's Worship and Other Essays*. London: Allan & Unwin, 1976.

Smith, Susan A. "Why Time Flies." *Psychology Today* (May/June, 2004).

Souhami, Diana. *Gertrude and Alice: Gertrude Stein and Alice B. Toklas*. London: Phoenix Press, 2000.

Statistics Canada. *Average Time Spent on Activities, by Sex*, 1998. www.40.statcan.ca/l01/cst01/famil36a.htm.

Tipler, Frank J. *The Physics of Immortality*. New York: Doubleday, 1994.

Travis, J. "Prehistoric Bacteria Revived from Buried Salt." *Science* (June 12, 1999). www.sciencenews.org/pages/sn_arc99/6_12_99/fob3.htm.

Waugh, Alexander. *Time: From Microseconds to Millennia, A Search for the Right Time*. London: Headline Book Publishing, 1999.

Webb, Mary. *Precious Bane*. London: Jonathan Cape, 1928.

Whittier, John Greenleaf. "My Soul and I." *The Complete Poetical Works of Whittier*. Boston: Houghton Mifflin, 1894.

Whorf, Benjamin Lee. *Language, Thought and Reality*. Massachusetts: MIT, 1956.

Winton, Tim. "Aquifer." *The Turning*. Toronto: HarperCollins, 2005.

Wittgenstein, Ludwig. *Tractatus Logico-Philisophicus*. [*Logisch-philosophische Abhandlung*.] Translated by D. F. Pears and B. F. McGuinness. New York: Humanities Press, 1961.

Yeats, William Butler. "The Second Coming." *Selected Poetry*. Edited and with an introduction by A. Norman Jeffares. London: Macmillan, 1962.

Index

Index